THE
COASTLINES
OF
BRITAIN

THE COASTLINES OF BRITAIN

Richard Muir

M

MACMILLAN
LONDON

For Kieran Rohan

First published 1993 by Macmillan London Limited,
a division of Pan Macmillan Limited,
Cavaye Place, London sw10 9pg
Associated companies throughout the world

1 3 5 7 9 8 6 4 2

© Richard Muir 1993

The right of Richard Muir to be identified as
the author of this work has been asserted by him
in accordance with the Copyright, Designs
and Patents Act 1988.

ISBN 0 333 54406 4

Printed and bound in Hong Kong

ACKNOWLEDGEMENTS

Grateful acknowledgement is made to the following for
permission to reproduce illustrations in the text:

pp. 33, 42, 158, 184, 187, 189, 197, 249 and 261 University
of Cambidge Committee for Aerial Photography;
pp. 164 and 167 © British Crown copyright 1993/MOD
reproduced with the permission of the Controller of
Her Britannic Majesty's Stationery Office.

All other photographs were taken by the author.

CONTENTS

Introduction   vii

 1 Where Land Meets Sea   1
 2 On the Beach   27
 3 Wildlife of the Sea Cliffs   45
 4 Life on the Beach   73
 5 The Wildlife of Dunes, Salt-marshes and Estuaries   101
 6 The Armoured Coast   121
 7 The Uncaring Sea   149
 8 Ports and Resorts   161
 9 From London to Land's End   193
10 From Land's End to John O'Groat's   215
11 John O'Groat's to London   243
12 Soiled Sands and Troubled Waters   267
   Some Useful Books   275
   Index   276

INTRODUCTION

Britain is a small country with a remarkably long coastline. Amongst our neighbours in Europe, Germany is a land-power with a modest sea frontage; France and Spain are larger than Britain but compact in shape, while Denmark has plenty of seaboard yet is in large part composed of islands. Even sea-girt Ireland and attenuated Italy cannot match the intricacy of the British outline. Not only is the British coastline exceptionally long and indented, it is also amazingly diverse. This has much to do with the varied geological endowment of rocks of all ages, compositions and strengths. Headlands formed of hard rocks of every major type are in plentiful supply, but so too are soft, low shores where dunes, lagoons, salt-marshes and mud-flats may form. And with this in mind, it is not surprising that seaside niches are available for a breathtaking array of wildlife.

This book is organised in such a way as to offer an introduction to every facet of the coastal scene. It begins with chapters which describe the physical forces that have created and shaped the visible scene. Once one has an understanding of the structure and resistance of the different rocks and of the way that the erosive forces of the sea behave, then it is possible to deduce at least a basic understanding of the origins of any well-loved passage of coastal scenery.

The chapters which follow are concerned with the wildlife of the coast: the birds, animals, fish, insects, molluscs, crustaceans and others, as well as the plants. It soon emerges that there is nothing random about the pattern of species in the galaxy of coastal life. Each one is precisely tailored to exploit a particular place in the seaside setting.

Next, we introduce man. Coastal life has always had a special spice and danger. Here we encounter men and women as fisher-folk, merchants, monks, privateers, smugglers and as the sponsors of resorts. A great many settlements are explored, and soon it emerges that spectacular changes of fortune are commonplace amongst the towns, villages and urban has-beens of the coastal strip.

Three chapters then provide a complete circuit of the mainland coast, highlighting places of particular scenic or historical interest, and seeking to encapsulate the character of the different sections of the coast.

The worst has been reserved for last, and although passing mentions are made of the disgraceful abuse and contamination of our shores in the preceding chapters, these are kept to a bare

minimum. A magical coastline which should be a source of national pride has been allowed to become a national disgrace – to the point where the most powerful supporters of a cleansed and revitalised shoreline are not found at Westminster, but abroad in the agencies of the EEC.

The United Kingdom comprises more than a thousand islands and islets. With this in mind, the decision to confine the text to the coast of the mainland island should not seem surprising. In a few cases of islands which are easily accessible and lie very close to the mainland, as with Anglesey and Skye, this rule is lifted. It is also lifted in the cases of the seabird colonies, where remoteness and seclusion were powerful attractions. And, of course, the principles of rock, wind and wave which explain the formation of coasts apply just as well to the shores of islands as to those of the mainland.

Chapter One

WHERE LAND MEETS SEA

A coastline is a meeting place between two very different worlds, those of land and of sea. It is also a world in its own right, though one which is much more confined. It has its own specialised wildlife, like cliff-nesting birds and sea anemones, and its own violent regime of land-wrecking and land-building. The coastline is a place with its own unmistakable ethos, be this based on the drama of Atlantic waves crashing against tall rock bastions or else founded on the dank lagoons and maze-like channels of an east-coast salt-marsh. It has its own economy and also its own societies, ranging from the dwindling communities of fisherfolk or dockers to those composed of returned and retired colonials with their seaside villas or the brash showmen of the less restrained resorts. Boscastle, Blyth, Bournemouth and Blackpool are as different as can be, but each has an identity forged by its coastal position.

The coastline is also a world on the move, though the movement is usually much too slow for us to notice the changes. Like rafts adrift on the currents from the inner earth, continents have cruised apart and buffeted together. Meanwhile, the seas gnaw and nibble at the continental margins, scouring out a bay here and then shaping and smoothing the eroded debris to form a sand bar or mud-flat further down the coast. But only when sea storms snatch a couple of metres of clay from the eastern shores or crack a sea wall to flood the houses which cower behind it are we really made aware of the transient nature of the coast.

At the coast, the bedrock of Britain stands naked and exposed. Take just a few steps inland and the foundations of scenery are blanketed by soil and masked by a living skin of pasture, crops, woodland and heath. Only the trained eye can deduce whether these foundations, which lie just feet or inches below our feet, are built of limestone, slate or sandstone. Yet at the cliffline, the scalpel of the sea has sliced a clean section through geological history. Here we can see great slices from that contorted layer cake of rock which records the history of the earth. There are great snowdrifts of chalk, corrugated and split by the same traumas

Huge blocks of limestone eroded from the cliffs above on a section of the Pembrokeshire coast; they will soon be reduced to a limey sludge by the action of the waves

1

Ammonite fossils dating from before the dawn of life on the land can be found in the cliffs at various places in the British Isles

which cast up the Alps; buttressed walls of grey granite, turned black-red by exposure to the salt spray; slumping masses of boulder clay, once smeared across the bed of a shrunken sea by ice sheets or glaciers, and rust-red conglomerates from deserts older than the dinosaurs, plum puddings of rounded cobbles set in a sandy matrix.

And within many of these rocks are the fossilised relics of life from different chapters in the earth's history. Scarcely any of these creatures were ever glimpsed alive by human eyes. Some tiny plants and animals were never seen by eyes of any kind and predate the evolution of vision. Dinosaur footprints, ammonites shaped like Catherine-wheels and which may be 200 million years old, trilobites more than twice as old and looking like giant petri-fied wood lice, tubes of coral packed together like fag-ends in an over-full ashtray and now exposed on a windy shore – these relics and many more can be seen in the great coastal museum of geology and evolution.

The mere fact that a rock is now seen exposed in our cliffs and beaches gives us no reason to suppose that it was actually formed on the coastline. The white chalks and silver-grey limestones accumulated from tiny sea shells which sank to the floors of shallow tropical seas. The granites solidified from great lakes of molten rock which were injected into fissures lying deep below the surface of the earth. Sandstones might just as easily have originated in desert dunes or been formed by eroded rock debris dumped in an upland lake by mountain streams as resulted from the compacted remains of seaside beaches. The great geological wheel of fortune, with its drifting continents, its land-building and land-breaking, has brought rocks with the most complicated life histories to places where they can be assailed by the waves and exposed to human gaze. Thus we find the red desert sandstones standing beside the cold, grey seas and iron skies of north-east Scotland; fragments of amber, fossilised resin from the ancient pine forests of continental Europe, littering the beaches of Norfolk; and the coal seams formed from swamp woodland which grew in steamy climates outcropping in the bleak shores of Tyneside.

The only constant is change itself. When mankind exists only as morsels in the fossil record, the granite cliffs of Cornwall may be eroded and washed away to become a sandy blanket on some ocean floor. And then at some more distant time these sands may be compacted into hard rock which then swells from the seabed on the crest of a great current of force to crown a mountain range. Cliffs of chalk and shale may blend in a sludge of mudstone, which might one day be a corner of some arctic continent. Nature is a great recycler of her building materials. The coastlines which we encounter now are seen in a brief snapshot of a tiny and insignificant moment in the cavalcade of time and change. Cliff, shore and beach seem timeless and enduring, but this is only because of the extreme brevity of our own existence.

Coastlines lie at the sharp end of this unrelenting recycling process, for there are few places where the wearing-down and rebuilding of rock and land proceed at such a frantic pace. One could sit and watch a river for weeks on end without being aware of the fact that sand particles suspended in the waters were slowly but surely grinding down the pebbles on the river bed. But when, from a cliff-top perch, one hears the clatter of pebbles hurled at the cliff base by seething waves or the rattle and sigh of shingle shifting in the surge, it is hard to ignore the stupendous forces of change. These forces are awe-inspiring but they are also apparently mindless. Why should so much energy be expended to remove a line of cliffs and then to employ the debris to build a new sand bar which may in its turn be swept away? Only mystics may imagine that they can see any purpose in all this – and they might well be misguided.

All we can know is that at some stage fairly near the beginning of time there was an earth and a sun. As the earth materials solidified to give rocks, vapours were released which condensed and then fell to provide the waters of the oceans. The sun provided energy: energy which ensured that air would be warmed and would rise, and so winds would blow and set the rolling waves in motion, to roll and roll until they collided at last with the land. In some way or other the earth acquired a moon and its gravitational pull gave birth to the tides. And so it will continue until the scorching heat from a swelling sun burns away the oceans and all the life that they spawned. And then the cliffs and beaches will experience the first rest they have had since before the dawn of life – until they too are consumed by fire. It is possible to discover how it all works, but the 'why' is a much bigger question.

Nature's wheel of fortune also determined that the coastline of Britain is anything but monotonous. The diversity of the British rock formations is astounding and the geology map of these islands is patterned like a patchwork quilt. All this ensures that in the course of a coastal walk of any length the rambler will see coastal scenes which are distinct and different. Anyone exploring the coast of North Wales and Anglesey will encounter up to a dozen major ages and types of rock outcropping in the shoreline. Tor Bay, between Torquay and Brixham, is less than five miles across, but those who walk around it will encounter limestone, sandstone, slate, grits, mudstone and a granite-like rock. It has been carved into the softer sandstone, slates and mudstones, while the tough limestone bracketing the bay forms bold promontories at Hope's Nose to the north and Berry Head to the south. All around the coasts of Britain one can explore scenes which geology students in many other countries must envy. As a student I could walk from Aberdeen to Stonehaven along some of the most dramatic and vertiginous cliffs in Britain. Most common were the bastions formed of very old quartz-banded gneisses and mica-speckled schists, both created by the baking and changing of yet more ancient rocks. In some places granite masses were ex-

posed in the cliffs, while in others there were great saw cuts or yawns where the sea had attacked an intruded rock sheet or dyke composed of less robust materials or had bitten into the weakened material along a fault line. But near Stonehaven one crossed the great Highland Boundary Fault and the whole character of the coastal scenery changed as the tough and incredibly old Pre-Cambrian rocks of the Highlands gave way to the hot desert formations known as the Old Red Sandstone.

One of the most celebrated sections of the English coast is at Lulworth Cove in Dorset, and here the spectacular scenery is very much a product of the local geology. The coast is hemmed by a narrow band of crumpled beds of Portland Stone – the same type of stone that was used for many of London's most prestigious buildings. This tough, cliff-forming band was breached at the mouth of the cove, allowing the sea to surge in and carve out the

An arch cut through the narrow band of tougher rock guarding the coast at Lulworth Cove

great oval of the cove in the weak rocks of the Wealden Beds lying just inland. Immediately to the west of the cove, at Stair Hole, one can see the same process being re-enacted, for here another arch-like breach has been cut in the protecting cliffs of Portland Stone and the sea is just beginning to go to work on the soft beds which they shielded.

Then there are also the contrasts which are more related to the earth history of a section of shoreline, to the rise and fall of the land or the coming and going of glacial conditions. Plainly, there is all the difference in the world between a low coast of drifting dunes, the mud-flats of an estuary, a shingle bank and a curtain wall of cliffs, and these differences can be explained in terms of what has gone before. In parts of Hampshire or places like Milford Haven in old Pembrokeshire the sea laps in sunken valleys which once had rivers flowing across their floors, while in the Western Highlands, old beaches and strand lines can be recognised standing high and dry several feet above the present sea level. Separating these elevated beaches may be long narrow inlets or fjords; sea lochs which are great trenches gouged out by glaciers as they ploughed their way towards a shrunken sea.

We are told that the Lord giveth and the Lord taketh away. Exactly the same can be said of the sea. In some places the coastline is of a 'constructional' type, for it is constantly being added to and enlarged by a retreating sea. In a few places the situation is almost static, and land-building and land-breaking have achieved an equilibrium. But in other places the sea is engaged in a remorseless attack on the land, and each crumbling of the cliff face marks a tiny victory in its eternal campaign.

The assault of the sea is mindless, but it operates within a strict framework of physical laws. If the sea had a mind and motives we could describe its work as an attempt to carve our shores and their approaches into gently sloping shelves. These slopes would be graded in just such a way that the erosive effects of the waves would almost be neutralised. All would be in equilibrium. In this sense then, the sea, like so many of us, is engaged in a perpetual yet unattainable quest for tranquillity.

The oceans were born when gases from a cooling earth condensed to form a rain that fell for perhaps 60,000 years. Around 3,000 million years ago, the torrential rainfall ceased – and so one might expect that by now the seas would have been able to grade their shores and come to rest. These efforts, however, are periodically frustrated by changes in sea level. When the great forces in

A sloping wave-cut platform at Kilve in Somerset, which is littered with debris eroded from the adjacent cliffs

the inner earth cause continents to crash and crumple and mountains to surge upwards, or when ice ages occur and lock up vast volumes of sea water in ice caps and glaciers, or when the retreat from glaciation releases great torrents of meltwater, then so the sea level changes. And then the sea must begin its work of grinding and pounding, sorting and dumping anew, all according to the new 'base level' which Nature has established. Unflagging and undaunted, the sea commences its toil again, unaware that further changes in sea level will invariably ensure that the task of grading the earth's shorelines will never even approach completion.

On many coasts we can see the stages reached by the work of the sea standing out quite starkly. At the foot of the cliffs we stand on a gently sloping platform which drops away very gradually towards the sea. Where now we find a smoothed rock surface and shallow rock pools, once there were cliffs. Those cliffs have been ground away, for all the energy of the sea has been directed towards extending the wave-cut platform landwards. At low tide we can walk across this rock platform towards the sea, and if the sea retreats far enough then we will come to a place where the rock becomes blanketed by sand. Some of the sandy debris eroded from the cliff far behind us has been used to cover the rock and thus extend the gentle angle of slope of the platform seawards.

The slight slope of this platform or shelf is at just the right angle to dissipate the rolling power of oncoming waves. The sea will continue to assault the cliff base and advance its platform landwards until the point comes when all its power is spent by the time the cliff foot is reached. Then it will only be able to undercut the cliffs on odd occasions when it is revitalised by storm and tide. But eventually its power to hack at the land will be exhausted and the cliff line will stabilise. This does not mean that the cliffs can now stand proud for ever. Although they are now immune from the sea's attack they are still prone to the much slower erosion by rain, frost and stream. And so, ever so slowly, they will lose the naked and vertical character of those cliffs which are under active frontal assault by the sea and will weather into more rounded forms and become cloaked by vegetation. Such rounded 'hogsback' cliffs are a feature of many coasts in Devon.

How exactly does the sea assail the land? By far the greatest part of erosion is achieved by waves. The energy for wave power comes ultimately from the sun. Variations in the way that different parts of the earth are warmed create great updraughts and downdraughts of air, with the heated air rising in the tropics and then descending. Pressure systems develop, with air being drawn from the highs to the lows, while the direction of the resultant winds is affected by the rotation of the earth. Winds blowing across the oceans create waves which, once set in motion, will continue to roll and ripple the surface of the waters long after the gales have ceased to blow.

Waves are the subject of some misunderstandings, for many people imagine that the sea water itself is moving forwards for mile upon mile. But in reality, the waves move whilst the water remains relatively stationary. Individual particles of water move in a circular fashion, rising to form the crest of the wave and sinking to form the trough. But they do not move forward very much. Waves and tides are also quite different, and tides are described in the chapter which follows.

As winds blow across the sea, the lowest level of the wind brushes across the surface, and friction with this uneven surface acts as a brake on the wind. The air just above is unimpeded, so that the different levels of air are moving at different speeds, and this creates a turbulence. The turbulence in turn affects the sea's surface, with the little skimming whirlpools of air causing ripples. The wind then builds up the ripples into waves, pushing them along, piling up water to heighten their crests and also whirling backwards down the slope of the waves to deepen the troughs between them.

There are three main ways in which waves achieve their effect. Water alone is a lubricant rather than an abrasive, so that in order to grind at a cliff the waves must be charged with a burden of particles which will produce the necessary friction. Under tranquil conditions, the power of wave and tide are quite sufficient for sand particles to be swept up and used in a corrasive fashion. But under storm conditions the power of the surges is almost incredible; masses of cobbles and boulders the size of footballs can be swept up and hurled against the shores. In 1852 a great sea storm struck Chesil Beach in Dorset and it is estimated that some $4\frac{1}{2}$ million tonnes of shingle were picked up and carried away.

As one would expect, the corrasive action of the waves is concentrated on the base of the cliffs. Here a notch is carved which undercuts the face of the cliff. The overhanging rock is subject to attack by the freezing and thawing of water trapped in crevices and by other forms of erosion, but, being undermined, it is also threatened by the force of gravity. Sooner or later, a section of the overhang will come crashing down, the sea will degrade and sweep away the debris and work will begin on scouring out a new notch.

The second form of wave action is quite different and operates through hydraulic principles. When a pounding wave strikes a cliff face then any pockets of air which are trapped in crevices are compressed. A brief instant later, the wave has broken and the compressed air expands again – but moments afterwards a new wave arrives. This repeated compression and expansion of air exerts a great strain upon the rocks of the cliff face, causing fissures to widen, until eventually a flake or slab of rock is exploded away. Perhaps the best way in which to experience the power of this form of erosion is to stand by a blowhole, like the Bullers of Buchan near Peterhead. Here a chimney has been blasted from the shoreline cave through to the cliff top. First one hears a wave crash into the foot of the chimney and then a great fountain of spray blasts upwards as though the cliff bastion were some vast blowing whale.

The third form is different again, being of a chemical nature. Sea water contains salts which are particularly effective against rocks of an alkaline constitution, the chalk and limestones. The chemical attack will tend to pick out details in the composition of the rock; much of the fine sculpting of the limestones of the famous

A finely detailed section of the Pembrokeshire coast near Lystep Head

Pembrokeshire coast results from this kind of assault. In addition, the swirling salt spray inhibits the growth of many plants in the vicinity of the sea, so that they cannot be present to shield and bind the rock with their foliage and roots.

The rate at which the sea is able to advance against the land is governed by a complex array of factors. Other things being equal, one would expect that the western coasts of Britain, which are exposed to the prevailing westerly winds and which bear the full force of Atlantic storms, would be retreating at a much swifter rate than the relatively sheltered shores of the North Sea. In reality, the reverse is true. This is largely because the west coasts are guarded by buttresses of tough old rock, while those of the east are composed of soft chalk, young sandstone, unconsolidated clays and the like. Some of the most dramatic rates of marine erosion are associated with the cliffs formed of buttery glacial boulder clays in the Holderness region. Here the coastal strip is retreating at an average rate of almost 2 m (2 yards) per year, though in the early 1950s in the area to the south of Bridlington a

land strip some 20 m (66 feet) wide was lost in the space of just five years. Since the start of the Middle Ages, at least two dozen villages and hamlets have been lost to the sea from the shores between Flamborough Head and Spurn Point. And since Roman times, the loss of land in the strip to the south of Bridlington has amounted to some 200 km² (80 square miles). Similarly rapid erosion has been experienced on the Lincolnshire coast in the Mablethorpe–Skegness region.

In complete contrast, there are western coasts which are subjected to far more vigorous buffetings but which are guarded by walls of hard basalt, granite or gneiss. Here erosion may be measured in centimetres per century rather than metres per decade.

Waves vary too. Their height and might will depend upon the strength of the wind which set them in motion and the length of 'fetch' or uninterrupted water across which such a wind was able to blow. The shores of the Northern Isles, western Ireland, the Outer Hebrides, Cornwall and north Devon have no protection from Atlantic waves and the length of fetch spans the whole ocean. This explains the attraction of Cornwall to surfing enthu-

With the sea being protected from the different winds by Anglesey and by the mainland of North Wales, the waves in the waters around the Menai Straits are of modest proportions

11

Pebbles and sand are washed up the beach in the swash

siasts. The shores of the Irish Sea, in contrast, are well protected because the maximum length of fetch is controlled by the protective presence of Ireland. Along the English and Welsh coasts of this sea the length is also affected by the direction of the wind. At Southport, for example, winds blowing directly from the west have a length of fetch of around 210 km (130 miles), the distance to the eastern shores of Ireland. When the wind blows from the north-west, however, this length is halved because of the shielding effect of the Isle of Man, and south-westerlies have a length of fetch of less than 80 km (50 miles) because of the presence in that direction of Anglesey. In Britain the steepest waves are encountered along the exposed Atlantic coasts, the gentlest in the shielded English Channel and Irish Sea, while those of the North Sea are of a moderate size.

Most holidaymakers realise that choppy seas can be encountered on days when the wind is only light. This is because waves, once formed, will continue to roll for quite some time and distance. The wave that breaks on a tranquil Cornish beach could be a legacy of a storm at sea which happened some days ago and 1,600 km (1,000 miles) away. Most persistent are the waves which have the longest distance between crests. Such 'free' waves can still roll in towards the coast when quite a stiff offshore breeze is blowing against them, and at such times the waves will be iced in white as the breeze blows back and disperses the crests of the waves. The last stage in the decay of free-wheeling waves comes in the form of a sea swell.

Storm waves have a great height between crest and trough, arrive in rapid succession with only short gaps between each wave and move quickly. As they encounter the shallowing waters of the beach platform the seabed exerts a drag on the rotational action of the waves. The breaking of waves occurs when they reach water which (if it were smooth) has a depth equal to about two thirds of the amplitude of the waves concerned. In this way a wave which has a height of 1.8 m (6 feet) between its crest and its trough will break in water which is 1.2 m (4 feet) deep. The crest of the wave rises to form a white wall of water, and as the drag increases this crest curves forward and plumets. Still charged with a forward motion, the breaking wave rushes up the coast as a 'swash' until its power to advance is exhausted, when its waters seethe back seawards beneath the next advancing wave as an undertow or backwash. All these motions can easily be recognised by an observer on the cliff top or sea wall. As well as producing a dramatic increase in the rate of assault on the cliffs, storm waves are outstandingly effective at removing sand and shingle debris from the beach. This is because they tend to break and fall in an almost vertical manner which produces a relatively weak swash but a very strong backwash. Waves associated with tranquil conditions

This backwash is towing eroding fragments of rock away from the shoreline

are, of course, lower and less frequent. Rather than towing beach materials seawards, they will tend to push them up the beach in their swash.

The effect of a particular set of waves upon a beach, this is to say whether the waves are building or degrading the shore, is partly governed by the frequency of the waves. Any observer can make a rough-and-ready guess at what is happening along the shoreline by using nothing more unusual than a wristwatch. Waves which are found to be arriving at intervals of around ten seconds will probably be of a constructive type, for the backwash of one wave has time to drain away before interfering with the swash of the next sand- or shingle-laden wave. However, when the wave frequency increases to a rate of about five seconds between waves then backwash does not have time to clear, and water running back down the slope of the beach collides with the swash of the oncoming wave just behind. Water gushes upwards from the collision and the power of the swash to drive debris up the beach is reduced, though beach material is still towed seawards by the backwash. Such destructive waves can be produced by storm conditions, but they can also form when the wave pattern is produced by two sets of winds blowing from rather different directions.

The approach to the shore and the configuration of the coastline are also important influences. When standing on the strand it seems that the distant, oncoming waves are running parallel to the shore. In fact, they usually approach at an oblique angle, but as they begin to encounter the shallowing waters of the beach shelf then the resulting friction or drag causes each wave to bend, so that the final part of the approach is roughly in line with the shore. The bending of waves affects the ways in which the sea grinds away the shoreline for, without going into the physical laws involved, the force of the attack is reduced in sweeping bays and concentrated upon the flanks of protruding headlands. However, once these promontories have been worn back and the resultant debris dumped to silt up the adjacent bays, the direction of the concentrated attack reverses. Then the sea scours back the bays until the headlands stand just as proud as before – but at the next stage in the cycle the promontories again bear the brunt of the attack. As the pendulum of wave erosion swings back and forth so the coastline retreats, but the alternation in the assault upon bays and headlands means that the general outline of the retreating coast remains more or less the same.

One does not need to be an expert to deduce that the sea's attack will achieve its most rapid advances against cliff bastions composed of rocks which are relatively soft, and encounter more resistance from those rocks of the harder kind. Where the cliffs have a very homogenous composition then erosion may proceed at a steady pace along extensive sections of the coastline. Much of the Sussex chalk is of this nature, so that one can find long, smooth white curtain walls of cliff with few pronounced projections or indentations. On the other hand, where rocks of different toughness are juxtaposed close together then detailed and dramatic sequences of coastal scenery are likely to be produced as the sea exploits the weaker beds. The coastline will have marked corrugations, just like the effects achieved by sandblasting a very grainy piece of timber. Nowhere is this effect better demonstrated than in the region of St David's in old Pembrokeshire, where masses of hard rock, which were intruded into the surrounding beds as a molten magma in distant geological times, have resisted the waves and project as bold headlands, like St David's Head, Pen Llechwen and Pen Clegyr.

Fast-eroding cliffs of yielding boulder clay near Covehithe on the East Anglian coast

The varying ways in which different kinds of rock are juxtaposed can have pronounced effects upon the coastline. If the upper section of a cliff stands upon footings of a soft, sticky clay and if the beds of rock dip towards the sea then severe landslips are to be expected. This is most likely to happen when the clay becomes water-logged and greasy, allowing the rocks above to slide seawards over their slithery base. A good example of this can be seen at Black Ven, near Lyme Regis, where beds of Greensand and Gault rocks have slumped over their treacherous foundations. The cliffs at Fairlight Glen, near Hastings, provide another example, with the Ashdown Sand rocks slipping on the Fairlight clay. Sometimes the rocks which have slumped seawards will form a step or undercliff at the foot of the original cliff, as at The Warren, near Folkestone, where the sea is confronted by a step of slumped chalk which fronts the intact chalk beds above and behind.

Finely detailed coastal scenery can sometimes be seen in rocks which have a homogenous composition. This is likely to occur if the rocks concerned are split by tiny fissures or joints or else riven by great fault lines which mark the places where a mass of rock has shattered and moved under the enormous pressure of earth forces. The waves will not fail to exploit such zones of weakness, until eventually great and dramatic gashes and inlets are carved.

At Huntsman's Leap, near Bosherton in old Pembrokeshire, two great cliff faces confront each other across a slender, precipitous chasm. Here the sea has assailed a vertical fault in the tough old limestone, surging inwards to carve a sheer-walled slit.

Differences in rock type can also affect the profile of a cliff. Chalk tends to be undercut by the sea and collapses in a way that produces near-vertical cliff faces, whereas clay produces cliffs of a gentler slope. At Flamborough Head, north of Bridlington, the chalk is capped by a thick layer of glacial boulder clay. The chalk weathers to produce the familiar sheer faces, but the boulder clay above is so soft that it erodes rapidly in the rain and frost and slopes away at a much shallower angle than the chalk on which it stands.

Rock strata dipping slightly to landward producing rugged cliffs near Filey

17

The slope of the cliff face will also be affected by the attitude and structure of the rock strata concerned. If the strata dips slightly in a landward direction then strong, steep cliffs usually form. But sometimes the beds of rock are shattered by a mass of hairline vertical cracks or joints. When this is the case, chunks of rock will sheer off as these joints are exposed, and in this way sloping cliffs will form in landward dipping strata. The cliffs known as Hangman Hills at Coombe Martin in Devon have a fairly shallow angle of about 45 degrees and are formed of sloping beds of grit which are full of joints.

Where the beds of rock dip towards the sea one will not expect to find sheer cliffs, just a sloping rock face. In such places the coast may erode quite swiftly, with blocks of rock sliding down the face as soon as they are loosened, to expose a new section to erosion by the waves.

The first stage in the chiselling of a coastal feature can be marked by cave formation. A cave will begin to form as the waves assault a weak point in the foot of the cliff face. This could be a patch of slightly softer rock or a spot where joints or a fault reduce the rock's power to resist. As the hollow in the cliff wall is deepened, so the blasting power of the succeeding waves, producing rapidly alternating rises and falls in air pressure, becomes enormous. The compression and decompression of the trapped air blows away fragments of rock, and so the cave becomes deeper and deeper. Thousands of excellent examples of sea caves punctuate the British coast, just one example being the sequences of caves carved into the chalk at Flamborough Head. At Flamborough one can also see a blow-hole or 'gloup', formed where the sea's blasting has undermined a part of a cave roof, allowing the storm waves to surge through the cavern and gush up through the chimney and into the air above.

Often the whole roof section of a long cavern which has been gouged into a line of weakness will collapse to expose a finger-like inlet or 'geo'. Huntsman's Leap, already mentioned, is a good example.

As we have seen, bands of tough rock will often project seaward as headlands or promontories. When caves form on each side of a narrow promontory they may meet to form a tunnel running right through the neck of the feature, which then becomes an arch. Such natural arches are not uncommon and are always spectacular. Well-known examples include the Green Bridge of Wales on a renowned section of the spectacular Pembrokeshire coast, Durdle

Door, near Lulworth Cove in Dorset, and the Needle Eye, near Wick. The eventual fate of such arches always involves the collapse of their roofs, and what remains thereafter is a pillar of rock which is now detached from the mass of cliffs.

These pillars are known as 'sea stacks' and they are far more numerous than the arches which still exist. Perhaps the most stunning example is the Old Man of Hoy in the Orkneys, which towers to a height of around 140 m (450 feet) above the sea. At the other extreme of Britain there is Old Harry, off the chalk cliffs of the Isle of Purbeck. In some places a succession of cave, arch and stack creation can produce a line of sea stacks, the first stack to have formed standing furthest from the shoreline. The Needles, off the Isle of Wight, are by far the most celebrated example of an alignment of stacks. There is the stump of a massive sea stack which is now stranded far to seaward of the cliff line on the beach at Tenby and a collection of stacks at Bedruthan Steps, near Newquay.

Some landforms of the coast, like caves and stacks, are easily explained in terms of the interaction between wave and rock, force and weakness. But there are others which are more complex and which were created by less obvious forces that might not occur to the casual onlooker. The great sea lochs or fjords which give the coast of the Scottish Highlands its deeply indented nature are an example. These are, in fact, heavily glaciated valleys which were subsequently inundated by a rising sea.

At the onset of glaciation – and Britain has experienced four major glaciations in the course of quite recent geological times – the mountains of the Scottish Highlands intercepted the blizzard-bearing clouds as they swept in from the grey Atlantic. Snow accumulated in upland hollows, where much of it survived the summer snowmelt and was gradually compacted and recrystallised into ice. As these hollows filled, so tongues of ice advanced downslope and were chanelled into the existing river valleys. Gradually, a great ice cap accumulated over the uplands, with long lobes of ice reaching down the steep western slopes as valley glaciers. The steepness of these slopes and the rapid build-up of ice on the high ground provided the conditions for the very active erosion of the old river valleys by the glaciers. They were deepened and straightened by the glacial gouges, with a U-shaped trough being carved into the floor of each valley.

When a glacier reaches the unfrozen sea then calving takes place, with blocks of ice from the snout of the glacier becoming detached and floating away as icebergs. During glaciation, however, the locking of so much water on the land in the form of ice resulted in a great lowering of the level of the world's oceans. And so the Scottish glaciers were ploughing seaward across land which is now covered by the sea. Meanwhile, the erosion by the glaciers was not simply governed by gravity in the ways that control erosion by rivers. Rather, there was a tendency for the glaciers to scour deeply into the middle section of a glen, but to leave a higher bar or threshold of land at the mouth of each valley. Now that the Scottish fjords are drowned, these bars are marked by shallower waters which then deepen as one sails into the fjords.

The over-deepening and inundation of the old river valleys of the north-western coasts of Scotland has created a spectacular pageant of loch and coastal scenery, but it has placed impassable obstacles in the way of direct land travel up or down the coastline. Thus the most direct way for a motorist to get from Kyle of Lochalsh to Mallaig, only about 32 km (20 miles) to the south as the crow flies, involves taking the Skye ferry to Kyleakin, driving across Skye and then taking another ferry across the Sound of Sleat. To make the trip by land avoiding the unbridged inlets of Loch Duich, Loch Mourn and Loch Nevis takes half a day and involves a massive detour via the Great Glen and Fort William.

There are also other important forms of coastal scenery which can only be explained by reference to the fact that sea level is not a permanent fixture. During the great glaciations, ice accumulated in northern Britain to the extent that in some places the ice caps were more than 600 m (2,000) feet thick. Even in the Pennines of northern England only the tallest summits stood above the ice as arctic black islands. The unimaginable weight of the ice actually had the effect of causing this peninsula of Europe to see-saw, with the northern section of Britain being borne downwards. When the ice caps melted and the weight of the great ice burden was removed, so the rapidly swelling seas flooded in. But at the same time the northern end of the see-saw began gradually to rise; Scotland has risen by several feet since the end of the last ice age and is still continuing to rise.

During the ice ages the most southerly parts of England were not glaciated, but with so much sea water being locked up as ice it is estimated that the sea level which existed then was some 60 m (200 feet) lower than that of today. And so the unfrozen rivers of the south carved their valleys downwards towards what, in modern terms, was a distant sea. It is an interesting thought that just a few thousand years ago forests were actually growing upon what is now the sea bed of the English Channel. Climate had warmed sufficiently to allow trees to grow off southern England in places which were as yet not inundated because much water was still lying frozen on the great land masses of the southern hemisphere. When the sea did rise it flooded the southern river valleys, which now exist as drowned valleys or 'rias'. Such rias can be seen from the inlets of the Wensum and Waveney in East Anglia via rias of the south coast, like the Cuckmere in Sussex and the Dart in Devon, around the Cornish coast and the great ria of the Severn estuary to Milford Haven in the south-west of Wales.

Meanwhile, as the sea was flooding in to drown the old river valleys of southern England and southern Ireland, the land in the north was very slowly rising towards the levels which had prevailed before the surface was depressed by the weight of the ice caps. In the west of Scotland this had the effect of actually raising beaches to levels which are now well above the reach of storm and tide. In many places along these shores the raised beach is plainly apparent. Walking towards the present strand one goes down a steep step which marks the former shore or low cliff line, then across a verdant plain of former sea bed before reaching the sea in its current situation. This fringe of raised beaches, manured by seaweed or kelp and blessed with fertile soils derived from sand and shell, has provided the crofters of the Highlands with a rich agricultural hem to a farming environment otherwise composed of ice-scoured uplands with pockets and blankets of sour, water-logged peat.

The raised beaches of Scotland can be understood by reference to events which occurred just moments ago on the geological timescale. There are many other raised beaches in Britain which were formed in far more distant times and which are far more difficult to interpret. The goal of erosion, whether on land or at the coast, is to level out the irregularities on the surface of the earth to produce gently undulating plains or slightly sloping shelves. But this goal is always thwarted by the great earth forces which can raise, lower and crumple the land. Throughout Britain we can find the relics of former attempts at levelling in the form of 'fossilised' plains and marine platforms which have been uplifted to counter all the work which erosion had achieved. Even high in the Pennines one does not encounter domed or crested hills but a series of plateaux linked by sections of steeper slope – and each plateau is an uplifted relic of an ancient attempt at plain or platform creation. Experts must work hard and long to decide whether such relics were levelled by the action of rivers or by the sea, but sometimes buried shingle beds may be found which point to a marine origin. It is even harder to relate the uplift of the plateaux to a particular event in the great geological calendar. However, one does not need to be an expert to realise that cliff tops often seem to mark the edge of a level plateau, so that as one walks along the cliff path one may go for miles without ever rising or descending more than a few feet. Frequently the cliff plateau represents a former seabed which has been uplifted and now stands far above sea level. Down below, meanwhile, the sea is slowly grinding at its shores in its blind efforts to carve new platforms.

Around the margins of Morecambe Bay in Lancashire a raised beach can be recognised at a height of about 6 m (20 feet) above sea level. Though a fossil, this beach is a relative youngster and like many Scottish and Irish raised beaches it was cut during the relatively high sea level prevailing after the last ice age. In Scotland the land has risen more than in northern England and on many parts of the coast benches cut by the sea can be traced at heights of around 7.5 m, 15 m and 30 m (25, 50 and 100 feet). It is thought that the fossil beaches at 7.5 m were carved after the last

ice had melted with the higher beaches being cut at earlier stages. Large fragments of these former beaches survive in various places, but around Oban Bay all three raised beaches can be recognised. In parts of Cornwall, and particularly between St Ives and Land's End, the land surface forms a plateau which ranges in height from about 110 m to 140 m (350 to about 400 feet). This plateau is generally regarded as the uplifted relic of an ancient wave-cut platform which is far, far older than the raised beaches of Scotland.

One of the characteristics of the northern and western sections of the British coast is the profusion of islands. Islands can be formed in a variety of different ways. One of the most frequent involves a rise in sea level to drown existing river valleys, so that a higher part of the old mainland which overlooked the valleys becomes detached and forms an island. The most important factor in the detachment of Anglesey involved the flooding of two ancient valleys to create the Menai Strait. The Isle of Wight was

The Menai Straits, valleys invaded and inundated by the sea

23

once part of the mainland, with its spine formed by a chalk ridge extending from Dorset and with the Frome flowing eastwards via what are now The Solent and Spithead. But a rise in the level of the sea relative to that of the land inundated the old valley of the Frome and since then the outline of the island has been reworked by the sea. Some smaller islands have also been created by the drowning of intervening low ground and river valleys, while others have become detached as the sea has eaten away at zones of less resistant rock.

The coastline is a most eventful place. It bustles with wildlife or else with holidaymakers and it is also a place of dramatic confrontation between the seemingly irresistible force of the sea and the apparently immovable mass of the land. Unknowingly and uncaringly, one division of the blind forces of Nature is engaged in a timeless struggle to batter down the ramparts of the land and grind hill and vale into a smoothly dipping coastal shelf. Yet at the same time another division ensures that sooner or later new land masses will rise and all the work of grinding and pounding will be undone. As we walk the coasts, with the vastness of sky, land and water reminding us of the brevity and insignificance of our existence, we see snapshots of moments of stages in the confrontation. If there is any ugliness in the panorama one can be sure that it is of human creation and even more ephemeral than the cliff arches or dunes. Otherwise, the blind forces are chiselling the granite bastions of Land's End at one extremity of the country, lapping against the Old Red Sandstone sea stacks of Duncansby, near John o' Groat's at the other and reworking all the shores that lie between.

Everything that we see, each little facet in the great pageant of coastal scenery has a story and an explanation. Very frequently one will need no more than the notions sketched out in this chapter to achieve a basic understanding of what is going on. And as it goes on, the sea not only displays its own handiwork but it also exposes what went on long, long ago. Thus, for example, beside Lulworth Cove in Dorset the sea blasts through a cave to reach a sheltered little beach where the cliff has been carved back to reveal middle-aged rocks which were crumpled into a big dipper ride of folds by the same great forces which cast up the Alps a mere ten to twenty million years ago. There is a great deal happening down at the coastline. It is a building site which stretches all the way around our shores, a place where the outline of the homeland is perpetually under review. And a place where change is the only constant.

*Rock strata contorted by
Alpine folding at
Lulworth Cove*

Chapter Two

Previous page:
Ranks of groynes
protecting a vulnerable
section of the Kent coast
at Reculver, where much
of the Roman fort of the
Saxon shore has been
washed away

I have described how rock fragments are ground away from the retreating coast by the remorseless attack of the sea – but what then happens to this debris? In the short term – geologically speaking – it is used to build beaches. And in the longer term it will be compacted to form new rocks and land masses as the great cycle of building and breaking rolls on and on. Beaches, as any bare-footed bather knows, are of many kinds. They can be of shingle, which rattles and slithers underfoot. They can be of coarse sand, grey, white, buff or golden. Or they can be of a finer silt, which clouds the swirling water and leaves muddy stains on the beachwear. Many an interest in the world of geology has begun in childhood by collecting pebbles on a holiday beach, for any beach worth its salt should offer a fair array of specimens. Some of the pebbles may match the tones and textures of the rocks in a nearby cliff, while others may be quite different and have been rolled and swept to the beach from places miles away. There may even be some with remarkable histories, like the Scandinavian stones bulldozed across the North Sea basin to the shores of East Anglia by advancing ice sheets.

Debris dislodged from cliffs can have many forms, ranging from fragments which are mere sand grains to angular blocks of rock from a collapsing cavern roof which are as large as houses. Once a chip or chunk of broken rock drops into the seething waves below it begins a long experience of being buffeted, rolled and pounded. As beach pebbles clatter together in the surge and swash, so all edges and corners are worn away, and each one becomes progressively smaller and more rounded. The destiny of each bit of shingle is to become no more than a pocketful of sand grains, but as it erodes, so it is also serving the sea as a tool to erode other pebbles and also those parts of the shoreline with which it comes into contact.

Pebbles are rather short-lived. A chunk of chalk detached from a soft cliff may be reduced to sludge within a year and a pebble of one of the less resistant sandstones may not last much longer. The tougher rocks are ground down to produce grains of sand and these grains are far more durable. Water is held between the tiny granules by capillary action, and this prevents them from banging and buffeting together unless they become stranded and dry out above the tide line. In this way sands can endure for thousands of years after chunks of soft shale or limestone have been degraded into muds and dispersed in the sea. The fine, granular composition of sand makes it an excellent protective home for many beach creatures. In comparison, the shingle beach is a relatively dead world, for as the waves pound over the shingle the pebbles crash together and crush any small organisms trapped between them.

On the beach, finely ground material from nearby cliffs merges with other forms of rock debris. The greater part of the sand found on many beaches is believed to have been carried to the sea by rivers, while some of it has been swept landward from the distant seabed. Chalk and shingle ballast which was dumped in water twenty fathoms deep lying 11 to 15 km (7 to 10 miles) off the coast of Sunderland was eventually brought to the shore by storm waves.

The beach is not a place where time stands still. Many a proud young sand-castle builder has returned from lunch to see the work of the morning swept away, and all the other sand and shingle on a beach is constantly being shifted to and fro. Sometimes, fine plains of sand which have accumulated during the gentle seas of summer will be scoured away to their rocky roots by the angry waves of winter. Beach materials are moved about in a variety of ways. Fine river and seabed silts can be carried by the water in suspension, while coarser fragments and pebbles are pulled and pushed in jerks and jumps as well as being rolled along the surface of the beach. The materials are moved up the beach in the swash and towed seaward by the backwash. But as well as moving up and down beaches they also move along them. This happens when waves tend to approach a beach at an oblique angle. When this occurs, the sand or shingle is washed diagonally up and along the beach in the swash and then seaward down the slope of the beach in the backwash, so that each grain or pebble gradually moves in a sawtooth progression in the longshore drift. The drift is essential to the destruction as well as the construction of coastlines, for if eroded material were not swept away from the cliff base it would soon form a protective buffer zone of debris, shielding the land from the assault of the waves.

Along the coast of the English Channel this movement of beach material is very marked. Waves tend to approach the south-facing shores from the south-west, this being the direction of the prevailing winds. Sand or shingle is pushed up and across the beaches by breaking waves heading towards the north-east, while the backwash moves them southwards, down the beach slopes. As a result of this sawtoothed movement the materials gradually progress from west to east along the Channel coast. This is easily confirmed

Land's End splits the tidal waters of the Atlantic

by looking at the way that sand and shingle have collected on the western sides of groynes or breakwaters along this coast, with these man-made obstructions to longshore drift helping to curtail the movement. Built of timber piles and rails or of concrete, the groynes are very effective in the accumulation of protective, beach-building materials. In fact, they can be so effective that materials collecting on one side of a groyne can build up to reach the height of the barrier, and so end its effectiveness until it is heightened. However, as beach materials are collected at one place, so other places further along the coast are deprived of sand and shingle to shield their shores, and rival resorts may find themselves engaged in groyne-building warfare. The evidence of such campaigns can be seen all along the groyne-fringed Sussex coast.

Tides have an important effect upon our beaches. Far out in the open Atlantic the range of the tidal movement is quite modest, only about 1 m (3 feet). However, as the approaching tidal waves encounter the shallowing waters of the wave-cut platforms, the inlets and the promontories around the coast, the range increases greatly. Two waves are experienced each day – or, more precisely, each lunar day of twenty-four hours and fifty minutes. Coming from the Atlantic, each wave is split as it meets the headland of south-western Ireland and then the southern branch is split again by the Cornish peninsula, one branch moving into the English Channel and the other into the Irish Sea. In this way different places along the coast have their high and low tides at different times. The pattern is complicated further by the counter-attraction of the sun to the gravitational influence of the moon; seasonal effects producing big tides at the equinoxes, and also by the ability of the wind to bank up water or else drive it from the shores. In spring tides, where the sun and moon pull the waters of the sea in the same direction, the average tidal range in Britain is around 4.5 m (15 feet). This figure falls to less than 3.5 m (12 feet) at neap tides, when sun and moon are at right angles and their pulls are opposed. However, the form and terrain of the coast can greatly magnify or reduce such figures, and where the tidal wave is progressively constricted in the tapering inlet of the Bristol Channel, the range between high and low water at the spring tide can be more than 12 m (40 feet).

In fact, tidal movements are very complicated and in the North Sea they involve both a form of wave movement and a sort of counter-clockwise spinning motion. There are three centres of spinning in the Sea, and at these places there are no tides, while the further one gets from the centres, the greater the range of the tides. There is one such centre midway between the Norfolk coast and the Netherlands, and at Lowestoft, quite close to the centre, the range is only about 2 m (6 feet). Near Felixstowe it has increased to around 3 m (10 feet), at Dover it is around 4.5 m (14 feet) and near Hastings the range has risen to around 5.5 m (18 feet).

Sand grains are continually being moved about by the waves and tides, many of them going nowhere in particular for tens of thousands of years. Some, however, escape the grasp of the sea. At low tide beach sands are open to the sky and they dry out in the sun. Where strong onshore winds are able to blow with undiminished strength across wide and exposed beaches, then particles of sand can be swept up and blown inland during a miniature sandstorm.

Where there is an adequate supply of wind-blown sand then a coastal belt of sand dunes may develop. At first the dunes, like those of the hot deserts, are unstable and mobile, gradually migrating as the winds pick up grains from their windward sides to blow streams of sand over their crests. Such dunes can engulf any settlements which lie on the line of their march. The port activities of Formby in Lancashire were curtailed by advancing dunes and similar threats proved too much for several communities. In 1413 a storm struck the shores of north-east Scotland and the winds set dunes in motion on the coast by the Ythan estuary. The church at Forvie village survived, along with the mansion of the laird, but all the peasant homes were engulfed by the sand. In 1850 gales caused the dunes on the Bay of Skaill on the main Orkney island to move, and the well-preserved relics of a fishing and farming village which was abandoned around 2450 BC emerged into the daylight.

Dunes become stable when they are colonised by the deep-rooted common dune-grass or marram grass. The roots bind the sands and the tufts of grass serve to trap grains driving in the winds. The marram grass is a valuable pioneer, and as the plants die and decay, so they contribute to the formation of a soil which can support more fastidious members of the plant community. Marram is often deliberately planted to stabilise dunes, and in this way the town of Formby was spared the fate which had befallen Forvie. It does, however, need regular supplies of fresh sand in order to retain its vigour and sometimes the planting of pines is preferred; their roots also bind the sand while their fallen needles blanket it. But such plantings can be unpopular with conservationists as they destroy the sand dune ecosystem. Marram gives a fragile form of protection and dunes can become bare and prone to move if the sparse grass cover is destroyed by the trampling feet of holidaymakers or if their sands are exposed in rabbit burrows. Often a coast is fringed by bare, young sand dunes while a belt of older, marram-covered dunes lies just inland. Dune ridges do not form the ideal kind of coastal protection, especially if the land behind them is low lying. In 1938 flooding resulted when the sea breached a narrow wall of dunes at Horsey in Norfolk.

The British coast includes many areas of dunes, some of them providing world-famous links golf courses. Morecambe Bay, Cardigan Bay, Braunton Burrows on Barnstable Bay, the Culbin Sands on the Moray Firth and the sands of Forvie to the north of

Aberdeen are among the most noted examples of coastal dune formations.

Some of the sand or shingle on a beach may be destined to accumulate in a spit or a bar and so can play a part in changing the outline of the coast. Not all the factors involved in spit and bar formation are agreed, but it seems that offshore bars are formed on gently sloping shores by waves which break well out to sea and sweep up seabed materials to build an offshore ridge. Bars run

From the air the Hurst Spit, in Hampshire, resembles the head of a sea horse

33

Orford Castle overlooks a stranded medieval port

parallel to the coast or across the mouths of inlets and eventually a bar may rise above sea level and completely seal off a small bay or inlet. The lagoon which forms in the low ground behind the bar will gradually be filled by river silts and will exist as salt-marsh before being drained and claimed as agricultural land.

Spits are rather different. They are attached to the coast and are composed not of seabed materials but of beach and river-borne materials carried along in the longshore drift. Spits begin as small tails of sand or shingle attached to the shore and gradually leng-

The ruined church at the lost Scottish port of Old Rattray

then, sometimes running parallel to the coast but sometimes growing away from it at an angle. They continue to grow until they reach water which is deep enough to permit the fierce sort of wave action which can tow away the sand or shingle.

Orford Ness on the coast of Suffolk is a shingle spit which runs southwards from Aldeburgh close and parallel to the coast. Beach shingle and river-borne materials have been moulded into the spit by sea currents and longshore drift, both moving southwards, and winds and waves from the east. As the spit grew, it deflected firstly the river Alde and then the river Butley southwards, with marshes developing on the low ground between the diverted rivers and the shingle wall. The spit is now about 17 km (11 miles) in length and its growth must have been quite rapid, for it will only have been a stump when Orford Castle was built as a costly royal stronghold in 1162. At this time the short spit afforded shelter to Orford haven, though later it grew to become a barrier to navigation and brought an end to Orford's prospects as a trading town.

Less well known is the case of Rattray, on the coast of north-east Scotland near Peterhead. In 1564, when the town was chartered as a Royal Burgh, it had bright prospects, a weekly market and twice-yearly fairs. Fishermen from Rattray worked off the Flemish coast, but their departures and homecomings were made hazardous by the accumulating sand bar known as Rattray Briggs. Within a century, the growth of this bar had caused the fortunes of the young town to tumble into steep decline, but a navigable channel must have been discovered, for at the start of the eighteenth century, Rattray folk had a high reputation for the curing of codfish. In 1732, however, sand clogged the harbour and shortly afterwards the little town was deserted. It is said that the channel to the sea closed so quickly that a ship laden with slates was trapped and the slates were used to roof a local farmstead. A lagoon, the Loch of Strathbeg, formed where the old bay had been and during the 1914–18 war the level of its waters was raised to allow seaplanes to operate. All that remains of the lost settlement is the ruined chapel built by the English adventurer, William Comyn, in the early thirteenth century.

The most remarkable spit is Chesil Beach in Dorset, which runs from near Abbotsbury to the Isle of Portland to form a 'tombolo' or an island tied to the land. The spit is around 26 km (16 miles) long and the precise nature of its formation is controversial. Longshore drift has swept beach shingle, some of it originating as debris from cliffs standing far away to the west, along the coast. The pebbles forming the beach have been sorted and graded by the sea, so that at the western end near Bridport they are grape-sized, while at the Portland end they are as big as tennis balls. Winds and waves coming from the south-west have combined with longshore drift to create this remarkable feature, which has 'captured' the once free-standing Isle of Portland. The height of the beach rises gradually from around 5.5 m (18 feet) in the north-west to more than twice this height in the south-east, and the waves have washed up subsidiary shingle ridges along the seaward flanks of the main ridge. On the landward side there is the long, slender lagoon known as 'The Fleet'. However, experts have disagreed about whether the beach grew in the manner of a spit or a bar.

Dungeness, astride the Kent and Sussex border, has a complicated origin, but it is clear that it has developed from the growth of a complex series of shingle ridges on its east-facing coast. This accumulation of shingle cut off the original bay, though traces of the old cliffline can be recognised at various inland places, such as near Winchelsea. In the shelter of the shingle ridges, the old bay was gradually filled with marine muds and then with river silts deposited by the river Rother and its tributaries. Here Romney Marsh developed on the low, soggy terrain, but continued silting and draining has reclaimed the old marshes. Since the end of the Middle Ages almost a mile of new land has been won from the sea at Dungeness.

Winchelsea or, more properly, New Winchelsea, is a fascinating case and its story is a reminder of the power of the sea over the affairs of men. The town was a deliberate creation, the brainchild of Edward I, who recognised that the original town of Winchelsea was fated to be swept away by the sea. This prophecy was fulfilled by a sea storm in 1287. The planned new town was set out around 1283 with a geometrical gridiron pattern of streets, these streets dividing the town into twenty-nine development blocks. There were three churches and an elongated market place. During the Tudor period, the town faced a perilous survival in the face of successive raids by the French and Spanish fleets, but its destiny was decided in other ways. Having removed the old Winchelsea by brute force, the sea adopted a more subtle strategy to attack its successor. During Elizabethan times, the harbour was gradually choked with silt and, deprived of the lifeblood of commerce, the town withered. By around 1700, less than one household in ten from the number supported in New Winchelsea's medieval hey-day remained.

In 1724, the spy, diplomat, adventurer and author, Daniel Defoe, described conditions at New Winchelsea: 'a town, if it deserves the name, which is rather the skeleton of an ancient city than a real town, where the ancient gates stand near three miles from one another over the fields, and where the ruins are so buried, that they have made good corn fields of the streets, and the plough goes over the foundations, nay over the first floors of the houses, and where nothing of a town but the destruction of it seems to remain'. Another noted traveller and diarist, Celia Fiennes, wrote a few years earlier that at New Winchelsea: 'there are very few houses but the Corporation still continues and the mayor and aldermen, which 13 makes most of the inhabitants.'

Just as New Winchelsea took over the trade of its doomed namesake, so Rye assumed the commerce which New Winchelsea could no longer sustain. But Rye too suffered the sea's displeasure and Defoe explained that: 'Rye would flourish again if her harbour, which was once able to receive the royal navy, could be restored; but as it is, the bar is so loaded with sand cast up by the sea, that ships of 200 tons choose to ride it out under Dengey or Beachy, though with the greater danger, rather than to run the hazard of going into Rye for shelter.' Now, in Winchelsea just

The sign of the Mermaid Inn is a reminder of Rye's seafaring past

twelve of the blocks around the much reduced church of St Thomas still contain dwellings, though here the fragments of King Edward's street plan are well preserved. Meanwhile, Rye, whose medieval walls were once lapped by the sea, now lies 3 km (2 miles) inland and plays host to tourists rather than mariners.

Salt-marshes represent a stage in the transition from sea to land. They were once a common feature of the British coast, though much old marshland has been reclaimed for cultivation. These marshes begin as broad sand flats, faintly sloping expanses of sand which are exposed at low tide. The change from sand-flat to salt-marsh starts with the slow deposition of fine particles of silt and mud upon the sands. At first, the accumulations of mud are small, low, localised and easily moved around by wave and tide. But gradually, larger and more permanent mud banks develop. These banks are then colonised by specialised plants which are

Salt marshes with winding creeks and with a protective belt of dunes on their seaward side on the Norfolk coast

able to thrive in the salty tidal environment. Eel-grass and samphire are often the first plants to become established. As these pioneering plants secure a hold upon the mud banks, so their foliage obstructs the waters which slowly seep back and forth with the tides, and this causes more fine silts to be deposited. The first plant colonists pave the way for other salt-marsh specialists, like the common salt-marsh grass or the sea aster, to gain a foothold on the rising mud banks. In due course, a rich plant community becomes established, as lavender, sea pink, sea plantain and wormwood arrive.

The gradients to the sea still remain very gentle, but as the mud banks rise, the sea cuts an intricate system of tidal creeks between them, the lack of steep slopes ensuring that these creeks meander in a maze-like manner as the tides draw water in and out of the marsh. In the days of the sand flat, the rising sea had moved

Cattle grazing on reclaimed salt-marsh below Brean Down in Somerset

across the area in a great silver sheet, but now it is splintered and channelled in a twining mass of salty streamlets. Mud accumulates around the plant communities, while uncolonised patches of ground remain a little lower, and in these places irregular ponds or salt pans form. The mud banks rise for so long as they can be over-topped by the tides, allowing their vegetation to trap the silt particles which build up these banks. Eventually, however, they reach heights which can only be submerged by the highest of spring tides and then their growth ceases. Such banks can often be identified by spreads of sea plantain.

The English coastal marshes were traditionally places of mystery and adventure, where smugglers would emerge at night from the mist-shrouded networks of creeks to land their contraband. They were also regarded as unhealthy settings, cold and damp in winter and infested with malaria-carrying mosquitoes in the summer. Writing about the old marsh-creek port of Conyer in Kent in 1778, E. Hasted reported that: 'Conyer's Quay is much used for the shipping of goods and corn from this part of the country. It has a very unhealthy air. The inhabitants are almost always subject to agues and are, in general, but very short lived.'

The marshes were regarded as important grazing areas from the earliest times. Sometimes they existed as great commons which were shared by the members of one or more village community and sometimes they were acquired by monasteries. In early medieval times, the marshes were often protected against flooding by low sea walls, but in the course of the thirteenth century, the climate became cooler, wetter and much more turbulent, and these old walls often proved inadequate. The records show that at Cliffe in Kent, where the monks of Christchurch Priory at Canterbury held a manor, bigger and bigger walls were needed to

Bridgewater Bay, with broad, sandy beaches and reclaimed salt-marsh to landward

41

An expanse of salt-marsh at the Beaulieu estuary in Hampshire, with cultivated land in the foreground

preserve the pasture. Clay was dug from ditches in the marshes and piled up on the seaward side of these ditches, with brushwood and faggots sometimes being used to reinforce the clay sea walls. In the shelter of these walls sheep grazed, the ewes being milked twice daily and the produce being used to make a popular cheese. The shepherds were the only other medieval inhabitants of the marshes, shelter being provided in the form of isolated huts or 'wicks' which were erected on patches of higher ground and ringed by drainage ditches.

Salt-marshes often develop in the shelter of a spit or bar, as at Westward Ho! in Devon or behind Blakeney Point in Norfolk, and they are also associated with estuaries. These are the meeting-places between the freshwater worlds of the rivers and the salty environment of the sea. Estuaries are also great dumping grounds for rock particles which have been eroded from the land and gradually transported seaward by the arteries of the drainage network. Some sand and silt will be swept down a river, deposited on a flood plain and later carried on again when the river floods or changes its course. Other such material has a more direct trip down to the seaside.

As a river merges into the brackish waters of the tidal zone, so the velocity of its flow is greatly reduced. It no longer has the power to roll or flick along the particles of sand and gravel which were moving seaward on the great conveyor belt of its bed. The finer particles which were being carried along in suspension by the waters of the river are then deposited, with the salty nature of the sea water causing tiny clay granules to coagulate and sink to the sea bed.

Other things being equal, the accumulation of enormous volumes of river-borne materials should lead to the growth of a vast delta of young land traversed by meandering and forking streams, such as can be seen at the mouths of the Nile or Niger: great fan-shaped plains which gradually advance against the sea. Deltas, however, are not common features of the British coast. For a delta to form, wave, current and tide must lack the power to wash away the sands and silts as quickly as they accumulate – and on the British coast these materials are frequently swept up and used in coast-building works elsewhere along the shore. Also, as I have described, many English rivers flow in valleys which were drowned by the rising sea after the last ice age. It will be a very long time before the submarine river valleys are so choked with silts as to allow deltas to grow at the junction of land and sea.

All our estuaries are, however, deltas in the making – places where deltas will develop if the estuaries ever become filled in by sediments. Estuaries are not only rich in sediments, they are also rich in nutrients. Were it not for the fact that estuaries, through their association with ports, refineries and related chemical industries, also often tend to be rich in pollution, then they would support many diverse and vibrant wildlife communities. Sea and river water do not simply blend together as they meet. Being less dense, the water arriving from the river tends to rise over the denser salt water, so that estuaries have a banded pattern of water. At the top there is the fresh water, moving seaward with its cargo of freshwater organisms. Next there is a zone of brackish water, which shifts landward and seaward with each shift of the tide, while at the bottom there is a layer of salt water, containing sea fish and crustaceans, which is thrust into the estuary on the rising tides.

Chapter Three

WILDLIFE OF THE SEA CLIFFS

The kestrel is a land bird which can often be seen hunting around sea cliffs

With its sheer slopes and expanses of bare rock, the cliff habitat is one of the most specialised that one can imagine. While rabbits sometimes have their burrows around the cliff top, mammals are not really equipped for the hazards of cliff life and the coastal rock faces are the domain of the seabird. Most of these birds are highly adapted and, although some individual species contain fantastic numbers of individuals, they form a small minority within the bird kingdom. There are just four great orders of seabird, compared with the twenty-eight different orders of land-living bird, and worldwide there are only 285 seabird species out of a total of about 8,600 known bird species. Some of the most spectacular seabirds – such as penguins, albatrosses and frigatebirds – cannot be seen in Britain, though others, such as puffins and gannets, can. Even the more drab and furtive of the members of the cliff community become fascinating once one learns a little about the details of their life-styles. Some seabirds are essentially birds of the sea and they shun the land except for the necessities of roosting and breeding. Other seabirds, such as gulls and cormorants, will habitually or occasionally desert the coastline to exploit inland resources, while cliffs can also harbour species which are generally regarded as birds of the land. These include members of the crow family, such as the raven, jackdaw and carrion crow, birds of prey, such as the peregrine falcon and kestrel, and some doves.

The nature of the different cliff habitats varies enormously. In some, the slopes are relatively gentle, undercutting by the sea has come to an end and a soil cover has developed to support a thick layer of vegetation. In such places the habitats will favour land creatures rather than cliff-loving species. Then there are the vertical walls of chalk, made of a rock which is relatively soft but which sometimes offers a few ledges or crannies. Some cliffs are too close to the clamour of seaports and resorts for the taste of many seabirds, but there are also mile upon mile of lonely coastline with gnarled, impregnable cliffs which seem to offer everything that the most fastidious gannet, fulmar or guillemot could wish for. And so it may seem strange that long stretches of seemingly inviting cliff appear relatively devoid of bird life.

Most seabirds are extremely colonial. In some cases the colonial instinct has produced the most remarkable assemblages of breeding birds. The population of Manx shearwaters on the small Dyfed (Pembrokeshire) island of Skomer is equal in number to the human population of a medium-sized town, such as Harrogate,

Herring gulls nesting amongst the cliff-top hummocks

while that of the gannets on little St Kilda is several times larger. While one can think of a variety of reasons why life in colonies has its advantages, a full understanding of the forces which concentrate seabirds in such masses while other areas are shunned is still to be gained. When grouped tightly together the birds have a better chance of protecting their eggs and fledglings against predatory birds, there are more eyes to scan the skies for trouble, and it may be that over time the seabirds have massed in those inaccessible places which offer the best protection against human disturbance and are within easy reach of the places where small fishes shoal.

Colonies of different species of seabird tend to favour the same stretches of cliff, with communities existing cheek by jowl. However, the different communities are seldom well interspersed and not only are they zoned in the horizontal dimension, but also vertically, with cliff sections and micro-habitats meeting the needs of some birds but not others.

Gulls often nest amongst hummocks in the short turf on the top of the cliff. In the earth which has formed at the places where the cliff top slopes down towards the rock face, puffins have their nest burrows, sometimes scooping out tunnels with their broad beaks and sometimes commandeering old rabbit burrows. In long-

Kittiwakes are more purposeful nest-builders than other gulls

established puffin colonies, the ground may become so pitted with burrows that it collapses. The storm petrel and the Manx shearwater also favour cliff-top burrows.

High on the sheer face are the nesting grounds of gannets and kittiwakes. Unlike some other seabirds, these are both nest builders, using seaweed and bits of flotsam which they plaster on to tiny ledges. Though gull-like in appearance, the kittiwake favours a much more maritime existence than most other gulls and its feet have longer claws, enabling it to cling to the smallest shelf or cranny. Because of the cramped conditions of its nesting sites, most clutches have only two eggs. Fulmars may also be found nesting high on the cliff, but they tend to require broader ledges than those favoured by the kittiwakes, and lay their eggs in hollows scraped in the earth which has accumulated on such ledges.

Gannets 'sky-pointing', a ritual which seems to safeguard the changeover of parents on precarious nesting sites

The lower levels of the cliff may be colonised by guillemots and razorbills. They do not build nests but simply lay their eggs on rock ledges, the razorbills preferring the less exposed crevices. Their eggs are more sharply pointed than those of other birds; this reduces the possibility of eggs being rolled from their niches. The young of these birds plunge from the nest site into the sea, before they are fully fledged, and so it is essential that the parents select a

relatively low ledge which directly overhangs the water. Any protrusions or cliff-foot boulders would make the first journey of the offspring a fatal one.

Although they have such strong social inclinations, most seabirds are also aggressively territorial. The territory, however, is far smaller than that defended by birds of the land, and consists only of the nest site and a few inches of ground around it. Because of the precarious nature of the site, a place which is more of a toe-hold than a home, peculiar behaviour patterns have sometimes evolved to prevent domestic disasters. Gannets, for example, indulge in a ritual of 'skypointing' when the time comes for one bird to exchange nest-sitting duties with its mate. Both perch close together and point their long bills upwards in an elaborate statement of intent which ensures that the change-over goes smoothly and that the nest or fledglings are not left exposed to predators.

All too often one reads of calamities for the coastal seabird communities. Most vulnerable are the guillemots, perhaps our most numerous seabird, which live in continual danger of oil spillages through their habit of swimming on the surface to plunge-dive for fish. Less well publicised, however, are the re-markable increases in seabird numbers which are due to less obvious causes. The most dramatic of these changes concerns the North Atlantic fulmar, a bird of gull-like appearance but really a member of the petrel family, which can be recognised by its long, narrow wings designed for gliding rather than for the 'lapping' flying motion of the gulls. Fulmars are birds of the open ocean, and were once confined to a few sub-arctic islands. Until they nested on Foula, the outermost of the Shetland Islands, in 1878, the only British colony was on St Kilda. In 1900, the birds became established on the gigantic cliffs of Hoy on the Orkneys, where nesting birds still spit regurgitated fish at any bold climbers attempting to climb the Old Man of Hoy. In the years that fol-lowed, fulmars advanced southwards along the eastern and west-ern coasts of Britain, with the Land's End region being reached in 1947, the Kentish coast in 1965, and the Isle of Wight in 1969. No definitive explanation for this remarkable expansion is known, although it has been suggested that the birds were first attracted to feed on offal from the old Greenland whale fishery. They may then have become ready to follow fishing fleets in search of fish debris. Though now widely distributed along the British coast, the largest colonies of fulmars, each with more than 10,000 pairs, are found on the northern islands of St Kilda, Fair Isle, Foula and Fetla.

The population of our most spectacular seabird, the gannet, has increased threefold during the last century. These are offshore birds which wander over the North Atlantic, while the young-sters, which are more footloose than their parents, range as far as the coast of West Africa. Now there are estimated to be around

150,000 nesting pairs, with some small colonies on mainland cliffs, as at Bempton near Flamborough Head, and six enormous island colonies, including St Kilda with 52,000 pairs, Grassholm with 16,000 pairs, Ailsa Craig with 13,000 pairs and Bass Rock with 9,000 pairs.

Some gulls are also on the increase. Both the herring gull and the black-headed gull have expanded their numbers in the course of this century, mainly by coming to terms with man's domination of the countryside and learning to prosper by following the plough and scavenging around rubbish tips. Many birds nest inland, some even learning to colonise chimney stacks. Unfortunately, neither man nor other seabirds have benefited from this expansion, for the birds can transmit harmful micro-organisms, and they also rob nests and displace less common seabird species from their nesting grounds. Britain now supports about 280,000 pairs of herring gull and perhaps around 200,000 pairs of black-headed gull, with some 100,000 herring gull being present in the Teesmouth area alone during winter. However, the most common British gull is the kittiwake, represented by about 500,000 breeding pairs, though since the kittiwake remains a bird of the cliff and sea it is less familiar to most people. It is another highly successful colonist with a population which has increased at a rate of about four per cent per annum in recent years. The kittiwake is named after its distinctive call, but the common gull has a name which is much less apt, for it is relatively uncommon as a resident and virtually confined to Scotland as a breeding bird. But in Scandinavia it is truly common, and vast flocks of Scandinavian birds winter in southern England in grasslands and beside reservoirs.

Sadly, the numbers of puffin around the British shores have been decreasing, though the decline of the northern puffinries may have halted. The puffin is a bird of northern latitudes and Britain lies at the southern extremity of its range, though some large colonies were supported here. In 1939 Lundy had around 3,500 of these birds, yet within three decades the puffin popu-lation had dropped to just fifty; here the decline was blamed on predation by rats. The large Scottish puffinries declined as well as the small colonies in southern England, but oil spillages do not seem to have been a major cause of the losses. Some experts have suggested that the birds were poisoned by long-life pesticide residues carried seaward in the river systems, which contami-nated the small fish eaten by puffins. St Kilda once supported up

Puffins nest in niches and burrows at the cliff-top

to 3 million pairs of puffin, but a recent count showed the population reduced to about 160,000 pairs.

It is doubtful if human predation during recent centuries has greatly affected seabird numbers, despite the large number of birds taken in former times. Between 1829 and 1929, the islanders of St Kilda took young fulmars from their cliffs at the rate of 10,000 each year. They were even said to have evolved abnormally long big toes to assist the scaling of the rocks. The fulmars were wind dried and then salted to support the community over the winter, and the birds also provided oil for lamps, feathers for bedding, and fat. Gannets, guillemots and puffins were also taken. Unknown to the islanders the 'sickness of eight days', which killed many St Kilda babies just after their first week of life, was found to be due to the habit of smearing the severed umbilical cord with a mixture of fulmar oil and sheep dung. Demoralisation and an inability to cope with the strengthening contacts with the world beyond were the main forces behind the evacuation of the depleted community in 1930. The taking of seabirds and their eggs played a vital role in the lifestyles of many other coastal communities. Since at least 1700, egg gatherers or 'climmers' worked Bempton Cliffs in Yorkshire and in 1884, some 130,000 guillemot eggs were collected here and exported to Leeds for use in an industrial process creating patent leather. Similarly, men from Ness on Lewis sailed to the islet of Sula Sgeir to take young gannets from the colony there.

Far more damaging than the old pursuits of the climmers are the disasters caused by oil spillages. When the *Torrey Canyon* was wrecked on the Seven Stones off the Scilly Isles in 1967, some 120,000 tons of crude oil were discharged into the sea. The oil slicks contaminated the Cornish coast and it is estimated that almost 10,000 seabirds were killed. Later, the *Amoco Cadiz* disaster claimed almost half as many bird lives. Less well publicised are the 'birdkill' events caused by minor spillages and the illegal washing-out of tanks at sea.

Puffins, guillemots and razorbills are members of the auk family, a family of birds confined to the northern hemisphere, which occupy environmental niches comparable to those commandeered by penguins in the southern hemisphere. There are three species of puffin, two in the Pacific and just the one in the Atlantic. Puffins are widely spread across the northern Atlantic shores, and in Iceland in 1950 alone, the islanders took some 250,000 birds from the cliffs. Smaller than most people seem to imagine, the puffin resembles some bizarre cross between a penguin and a parrot, but unlike the flightless penguin it is an accomplished flier, and birds may be seen making a dart-like progress on whirring wings. The puffin's most striking feature is its broad bill, banded in red and blue. Developed for display and for excavating the breeding burrow, the coloured beak appears during the breeding season, when a showy sheath, which is later shed, grows over the drab winter bill. Because of its striking bill, the puffin has acquired a range of local names: sea-parrot, bottle nose, coulter neb and tommy noddy, to name but a few.

The nest is in a burrow on the grassy slopes of the cliff top, and hardly any nesting material other than a few feathers and blades of grass is used. Just a single egg is produced by the pair each year, and the long incubation period of about forty days is followed by a further period of forty days before the nestling is ready to leave its burrow. This it does under some duress, for when the parents sense that it is ready to go they cease to bring it food. Meanwhile, the bustling and quarrelsome parents defend the opening of the burrow fiercely, and sometimes squabbling pairs of puffin topple from the cliff locked in a combat which continues until the birds are halfway to the sea. In order to feed the chick the puffin parents fish the waters within about 30 km (20 miles) of the nest site for sand eels and sprats, somehow managing to bring back up to a dozen small fish, arranged cross-wise in their beaks, at one time. During the return flight they may have to brave gulls and jackdaws which quite literally attempt to steal the food from their mouths.

The guillemot is a very common seabird, but one which seems to be declining slightly, perhaps as a consequence of oil pollution incidents. It is unusual and puzzling in that the common guillemot can be seen in two colour forms, one with a black head and back and white breast, and a 'bridled' form in which a white collar extends back around the neck as far as the roots of the wings. Bridled birds do not belong to separate species, but they are absent among the Pacific communities of the birds and vary in frequency elsewhere; in southern England they form only one per cent of the population but in south-west Ireland they form half the total. Guillemots lay a single egg on a bare rock ledge, and the parents defend the immediate vicinity of the nest against other members of the colony with stabbing thrusts of their pointed bills. Several days before it hatches, the embryo guillemot learns to recognise the individual call used by its parents only for communication with their offspring. When just a fortnight old the young bird plunges from the nest site into the waves below.

The black guillemot has only a small wing patch of white and is a more solitary and adaptable bird. It does not form large colonies like those of its cousin, but lives in small groups or as isolated pairs. Black guillemots nest in crevices, caves and boulders at the base of cliffs as well as in ruined walls and jetties. The breeding population amounts to about 10,000 pairs. The Northern Isles are the stronghold of this largely Scottish bird, although fairly recently black guillemots have expanded down the west coast of Britain and populations have been established on Anglesey and the Isle of Man.

Wherever one finds guillemots one is almost certain to find razorbills, even though the guillemots nest on the open cliff and the razorbills in less exposed nooks and crannies among broken rock. When the razorbill chick is just two or three weeks old and only a third grown it is lured from its nest site by the cries of its parents as they bob about in the sea. Although they resemble guillemots in their form and plumage, razorbills have much thicker and blunter bills. Britain is home to a considerable pro-

A congested colony of guillemots

portion of the world's population of razorbills, though the birds seem to be decreasing along many coasts, perhaps as a result of overfishing by man.

One member of the auk family, the little auk, is the most numerous bird in the North Atlantic, and possibly the most numerous bird in the world. One colony in Greenland has well over a million pairs. Britain, however, is just beyond the southern limits of the breeding range of this bird, although modest numbers visit Shetland between November and February. When driven across the cold seas by winter gales, individual waifs may be spotted almost anywhere along the British coast.

One cannot leave the auk family without mentioning the legendary great auk or garefowl. This bird stood almost 1 m (3 feet) tall, was flightless and resembled a strange cross between a razorbill and a penguin. In prehistoric times, colonies were found along the European coasts, but it became confined to St Kilda – though there were other colonies in Canada, Iceland, Greenland and the Faroes. The Newfoundland colony was substantial and visiting sailors would provision their ships by marching large numbers of ill-fated auks up the gangplank – in fact in such large numbers that by 1800 the birds had disappeared from the island. In the second half of the seventeenth century, great auks were still nesting on St Kilda, but then they became uncommon there; the last British survivor was clubbed to death in 1840 by two islanders who mistook the unfamiliar bird for a witch. Four years later, the great auk became extinct when a breeding pair were killed and their solitary egg was broken on an island off Iceland. Victorian naturalists fully expected that birds could be rediscovered and preserved in some sub-Arctic fastness, but the great auk was never seen again.

Britain and Ireland are the main strongholds of the North Atlantic gannet. These birds have been around for a very long time for, like many other surviving bird species, they appeared in the Miocene period, between twenty-five and eleven million years ago. Despite its long existence, in quite recent years the gannet has been actively involved in changing its range. It was only at the start of this century that colonies were established on Shetland, and in 1937 that the small one on Bempton Cliffs was founded. On the west coast of England and Wales, the colony on Lundy was deserted during the nineteenth century, but at the same time a new one formed on Grassholme. The range of the gannet now extends southwards to include the Channel Isles.

These birds are not prolific; gannets may not breed until their fourth year and then only one egg is laid. It takes six or seven weeks to hatch and about 135 days pass between the egg being laid and the fledgling being ready to fly, so that only one brood can be produced each year. When on the nest, the parent sits with its feet overlapping on the egg, these feet being unusual in that the webbing extends to the rear claw. Gannets catch fish by plummeting into the water from heights of 30 m (100 feet) or more, and in order to withstand the impact they have specially strengthened skulls. The long, pointed, black-tipped wings resemble those of a glider and are designed for a gliding flight, with the birds soaring gracefully around the cliff on air currents before folding their wings and plunging on their prey. Fish are carried back to the nest in the throat of the gannet, and the young bird obtains its food by forcing its bill inside that of the parent. The young gannet has mottled brown plumage which it retains until its fourth year. If it is unable to launch itself directly from the nest it must brave the stabbing beaks of its neighbours before taking to the sky. It departs with sufficient fat reserves to sustain it for three weeks and, during this time, it must teach itself all the technicalities of fishing and flight without any parental supervision.

The cormorant is most widely known because of the use of captive birds for fishing in China and Japan, the birds being held on a line which is attached to a collar that prevents them from swallowing their catch. Fewer people may know that cormorants are relatively common in British waters – and fewer still that cormorants were used for fishing here as sporting birds in Stuart times, when the kings appointed a Master of Cormorants. The family of cormorants and shags includes some twenty-nine different species worldwide, the largest being the common cormorant, found in Britain and around 1 m (40 inches) in length. The cormorant has dark, iridescent plumage, a small white patch on its upper leg and a bare patch of white skin at the base of its slightly hooked bill. The somewhat smaller green cormorant or shag is born black and naked, then acquires brown down and then a set of brown feathers before the bottle-green adult plumage arrives. At the start of the breeding season a short crest is grown. Both cormorants and shags are accomplished divers, following their prey with their necks extended and wings folded back, while using their webbed feet as paddles. Cormorants are believed to pursue fish at depths of up to 30 m (100 feet), while shags can remain under water for well over a minute. However, they do not compete for exactly the same ecological niche. The cormorant takes a high proportion of flat fish, while the shag prefers sand eels. And the shag favours a more maritime life style, only straying inland from its footholds on the north-western shores when driven by gales. The cormorant is more widely distributed, often fishes in lakes and estuaries and can be seen on almost any British coastline in the winter, when there is an influx of cormorants from the continent. Caithness is the main stronghold of the cormorant and supports about a thousand breeding pairs. The shag has its British heartlands at the extremities of the islands, with Shetland and the Isles of Scilly each having about a third of the population.

The seabirds described in the paragraph which follows are remarkable for their adaptation for a life spent above or among the waves. Some of them accomplish the most extraordinary journeys, and though all of them are little-known to the public at large, they exist in considerable and flourishing numbers, it being only their life-styles which make them unfamiliar. Were it possible for them to breed on the ocean's swell then none of these birds might ever choose to set foot on land, and when they do arrive here they select the places most immune from disturbance by mammals, whether of the four-legged or the two-legged kind.

One of the most fascinating of the British seabirds is also one of the least likely to be seen. The storm petrels are divided into twenty-two species, one of which, the Wilson's petrel, is another claimant to the title of the world's most numerous bird, although this wanderer from the Antarctic is only rarely reported in Britain. The British storm petrel is seldom seen because of its strongly oceanic life style and its habit of only visiting its remote breeding colonies after night has fallen. It is most likely to be glimpsed from boats at sea or when flocks of these small birds are driven inland by storms. Looking rather like a very small, dusky, web-footed pigeon, the storm petrel breeds on small and lonely islands from Iceland to the Canaries, including those off the northern and western shores of Britain. Nests are made in crevices in cliffs, in long-deserted buildings or in burrows excavated by the birds, and but a single chick is reared each year. The name 'petrel' seems to derive from St Peter and may relate to the way in which the birds seem to be walking on water as they scour the wakes of ships for morsels of food churned up by the propellers. On land, however, it has great difficulty in walking and can only do so with support from its fluttering wings. To sailors, storm petrels are also known as 'Mother Carey's chickens', a name deriving from the Blessed Virgin Mary or 'Mater Cara'. Leach's petrel is less common, and breeding colonies are confined to the loneliest of islands, like St Kilda, Sule Skerry and Foula; it can be distinguished from the slightly smaller British storm petrel by its forked tail.

The fulmar has already been mentioned, and there are several other seabirds which might be mistaken for gulls. Like petrels, shearwaters are small birds which are far better equipped for a life ranging across the oceans than living on land. Only a minority of British people may have heard of the Manx shearwater, and yet it is much more numerous than some familiar birds; in 1968, 135,000 pairs were counted on two little islands off the Dyfed (Pembroke-shire) coast, and other large colonies exist on small islands from the Isles of Scilly to the Shetlands. This figure seems modest when compared to the three million related great shearwaters which nest on the tiny Nightingale Island in the Tristan da Cunha group. Manx shearwaters are unfamiliar to all but sailors and yachtsmen because they spend most of their lives far from sight of land and nest in burrows in the turf capping of remote cliffs, under boulders, on inaccessible rocky promontories or near the tops of mountains. Blackish above and white below, the shearwater has a slender, slightly hooked bill and webbed feet but is most easily recognised when seen in flight, when it seems to flicker as its dark and light surfaces are alternately exposed. The wings are long and slender and serve the birds well for their far-ranging flights. Young birds ringed on Skokholm arrived in Brazilian waters within weeks of leaving their burrows, while one bird was found to have reached Australia. At least three other shearwaters, Cory's, the great and the sooty, visit Britain as migrants in passage; the first named *en route* from the Mediterranean to the Grand Banks or even the Cape of Good Hope, the second from Tristan da Cunha to the Grand Banks and the third from New Zealand or Patagonia to the North Atlantic.

Skuas are closely related to sea gulls and are parasitic scavengers which harry smaller and less aggressive seabirds until they surrender their hard-won morsels of food. Despite its unappealing occupation, the Arctic skua is a fascinating bird. Black-legged and gull-like in appearance, it occurs in a range of different colour phases. The lightest phase displays a black cap and tail, yellowish neck, white body and grey wings, while the darkest phase is almost completely sooty. Birds of different phases will interbreed, but they seem to prefer mates of their own colour. On Shetland, home to half the British population, a quarter to a third of the birds belong to the light phase, with this proportion increasing as one moves northwards through the breeding range of the Arctic skua. These changes cannot be attributed to the isolation of colonies, for the skuas travel widely, from arctic latitudes to the shores of the South Atlantic. Although they tend to nest on moors and heaths close to the coast, skuas are classed here amongst the seabirds of the cliffs because it is here that one is most likely to see them enacting their role as the muggers of the bird kingdom. The species is on the increase and breeds in the Northern and Western Isles but can occur almost anywhere as a passage migrant in late summer and autumn. Such migrants are particularly likely to appear when large numbers of sand eels attract flocks of terns to estuaries.

With about 4,000 pairs breeding in Britain, the great skua is four times as numerous as its smaller cousin. A more formidable bird, almost 60 cm (2 feet) in length, it not only follows fishing fleets for offal, harries birds for food, steals eggs and chicks, but will also kill adults of smaller seabird species. Mainly a dull brown in colour, the great skua can be distinguished from immature large gulls by its small but prominent white wing patches. Like the Arctic skua, the great skua is enjoying a period of success and expansion, and though it was restricted to Foula in Victorian times it has now spread throughout the Northern Isles and Outer Hebrides and has established mainland colonies in Sutherland. Foula still remains the favoured stronghold, supporting around

Herring gulls raucously proclaim their ownership of a nesting territory

2,500 pairs where only around a hundred existed a century ago. Support from pioneering conservationists must have helped the spread of the great skua, although the whole population of the bird appears to be shifting southward and the Icelandic population is declining.

The great skua pair lays two or three eggs in a grass-lined depression on moorland, and all their aggression is focused on defending the nest site, so that even human visitors are fiercely mobbed. These birds also travel widely; one ringed on Foula turned up in Guyana, whilst great skuas from the southern hemisphere population reach western Canada and Japan. The long-tailed skua only breeds in sub-Arctic fastnesses when the rodent population there is large enough to support the family. Otherwise it spends its life at sea, but is sometimes glimpsed around the coasts of eastern England, although the main wintering areas are off the coasts of Argentina and Chile. Two long feathers give a swallow-like extension to its tail. The Pomarine skua has longer feathers in the centre of its tail and is another great rover. Like its long-tailed cousin, it nests on the frigid coasts of Canada and Siberia, but in winter it can be found off West Africa, New Zealand and Peru. These birds are quite often seen off the British coasts, many being spotted in early May by bird watchers on the headlands of the west coast.

Gulls are the birds which most people will think of first when asked to mention a seabird – although many gulls are far less specialised as mariners than the petrels, shearwaters and skuas.

The members of this raucous family are distributed throughout the world and there are some forty-two different species. Gulls have proved to be remarkably successful birds, and some enormous colonies exist; in 1969, 17,500 pairs of lesser black-backed gulls and a similar number of pairs of herring gulls were counted nesting on Walney Island alone. The main species of gull are also increasing, sometimes in a most dramatic fashion. This is not because they are particularly rapid breeders; some take four years to reach maturity and most lay just two or three eggs. However, the birds are long-lived and also seem to have adapted to modern conditions. Gulls vary in the strength of their orientation towards maritime life and their readiness to embark on long journeys. Kittiwakes are seldom seen inland and Sabine's gull, sometimes arriving as a migrant in passage, crosses the Atlantic from North America to winter off the coast of West Africa. The lesser black-backed gull is another migratory gull. Three-quarters of the British breeding population of this bird nest on Walney before migrating south-westwards in the autumn. In contrast, the herring gull, which is the gull most frequently seen in England, has a much less footloose and maritime lifestyle. It will nest on cliffs but can also be found on the low coasts of the south-east, and it even breeds in central London, while every fishing port has its own resident population of herring gulls. Members of inland herring gull colonies may feed within a few kilometres of their nests, often on refuse tips, and so scarcely qualify as seabirds.

Most gulls have strong colonial instincts, though within the colony their behaviour may seem highly anti-social. While the members of a colony will rally to drive off a hostile intruder, each nesting pair within the colony will ruthlessly defend its own tiny territory. Neighbours know the limits of their own particular territories to an inch, and will not attack chicks wandering within an adjacent territory – yet any chick which trespasses beyond its parental sphere is likely to be killed by the folk next door. Within the colonies, various forms of behaviour have evolved. Black-headed gulls, for example, take great care to remove the shells of hatched eggs from the vicinity of the nest, since the presence of egg shells apparently encourages predators, such as the carrion crow, to come and steal unhatched eggs. Herring gulls have a red blotch on the undersides of their bills and these blotches stimulate chicks to peck at the bill to beg for food, and this in turn stimulates the parent to regurgitate food.

The success of the British seagull communities has created a

Gulls are slow to obtain their adult plumage. This black-headed gull is just starting to acquire the distinctive black headgear

number of problems. This is certainly true in the case of the great black-backed gull. In the 1930s, Britain supported around 700 breeding pairs, but in 1970, some 22,000 breeding pairs were counted. This is a fiercely predatory bird and in one Welsh location it was found that Manx shearwaters formed forty-five per cent of the birds' diet, puffins two per cent, while rabbits provided sixteen per cent of their food. On the east coast great black-backed gulls wrought havoc amongst the colony of rare avocets, taking nearly all the chicks hatched until a campaign of destroying the nests of the gulls responsible was launched. The largest colony is on North Rona and there are large colonies on the Scilly Isles; the birds breed at many sites on the west coast and elsewhere in Scotland, and can often be seen as non-breeders along the south and east coasts. People seeing one of these birds for the first time are likely to be amazed by its size, for this is the largest of the gulls and measures some 75 cm (30 inches) in length. Other gull problems include the health hazards posed by herring gulls, which may pollute reservoirs with salmonella after scavenging on refuse tips, and the danger of bird strikes (collisions between aircraft and birds) resulting from the peculiar attraction of airfields to members of the tribe, such as the common gull.

During the early stages of their life, gull chicks are remarkably advanced for their age and some can wander from the nest within a day of hatching. At first, the chicks have a mottled, camouflaged down in shades of buff, brown or grey, which makes them difficult to spot amongst sand and pebbles. Several weeks later, the down is shed and replaced by plumage which is generally of a speckled brown colour. The immature coloration is then retained for a long time – for four years in the case of the great black-backed gull. The glaucous gull remains the colour of milky coffee until its fifth year, becoming a little paler with each moult.

Some gulls, like the kittiwakes and great black-backed gulls, are cliff-nesters but others prefer life on the horizontal rather than the vertical plain. (Though very numerous around the coast, the kittiwake does not seem to have developed the opportunistic nature seen in other gulls, but it may still adjust itself more closely to exploiting the man-made world.) The black-headed gull favours marshes, moors, dunes and tussocks on shingle banks and the common gulls like similar sites, though they have been known to take over abandoned nests in trees. Herring gulls and lesser black-backed gulls also like such places, but they will nest on sheer cliffs too.

The gulls mentioned in the preceding paragraph are all numerous as breeding birds in Britain, but there are other gulls which are much more rarely glimpsed. The little gull is the smallest of the world's gulls, just 25 cm (10 inches) long, and a very rare breeder in Britain, where it has nested around the Ouse Washes and the Wash. Its main range extends south-eastwards into Asia, but flocks may be storm-driven to the eastern coasts of Britain. Sabine's gull is a passage migrant which can instantly be recognised, for while its body has the familiar white, grey and black colouration, its head is grey and defined by a narrow black neck band. The Mediterranean gull has occasionally nested in Hampshire, where individuals have also hybridised with members of resident black-headed gull communities. The Iceland gull and the larger glaucous gull are the only gulls that are white with silver-grey wings which lack the customary black tips, while the ivory gull is the only pure-white gull. The first named is a rare winter visitor to the far north and the glaucous gull is seen rather more frequently and spreads further south, even arriving at the Channel in harsh winters. The ivory gull is a bird of the open seas which is sometimes driven to the northern coasts by storms.

Finally, one may be surprised to find nesting close to a cliff community of birds such as kittiwakes, a pair or more of doves, even though such birds are quite unequipped to fish and are more generally associated with leafy countrysides and urban environments. These birds will belong to one of two species which are confusingly alike in appearance and name. However, stock doves, though expanding northwards, are most common in southern and eastern England and are not found north of Inverness. Wild rock doves inhabit the coasts of northern and western Scotland – but they are also the ancestors of the London pigeon and all those other flocks of urban pigeons. As a result, any dove-like bird seen nesting on cliffs in England is quite likely to be a feral London pigeon which is rediscovering the habits of its ancestors. The stock dove is comfortable in agricultural countryside as well as in cliff settings and, despite the opportunism and adaptability of its town-dwelling relations, the wild rock dove is a bird of the coast. The rock dove can be distinguished from all other members of the tribe of doves by its white rump. The stock dove is a blue-grey colour with a pinkish breast and its black wing tips and tail help to distinguish it from the rock dove. Both birds are gregarious, the stock dove often flocks with wood pigeons and the rock dove nests in cliff colonies. Unlike other birds of the rocky coast, the doves have diets which are basically vegetarian and will fly inland to plunder crops if the opportunity arises, although the rock dove will take animal food, like snails and the eggs of whelks.

There are very few conventional plants which can pass the rigorous tests necessary for survival in the harsh sea cliff habitat. The hardships are both varied and severe. First of all there is the chemical problem posed by the saline spray, which is swirled and lashed around the cliffs as gales sweep across the surf. This problem alone is sufficient to evict trees from steep cliffs which they might otherwise colonise. Then there is the absence of all but the smallest pockets of soil amidst the sheer expanses of rock. Even such footholds as may exist are likely to have soils of a rather extreme type, with strongly alkaline soils forming in the crannies of chalk and limestone, while gritty, acidic soils develop in granite cliffs. The closeness of the link between the soils and the geology of the cliff means that cliffs cut in alkaline rocks can be expected to support plant communities which are quite different from those growing on cliffs formed of acidic rocks. And then there are the accumulations of guano associated with seabird communities, which over-enrich the soils to the point where they are poisonous to plants. To all these discouragements to plant growth can be added the factors of trampling by seabirds and severe exposure to winds, which arrive unchecked from the open sea to batter and whirl against the cliffs.

And yet the prospects for plant life are not entirely bleak. Cold as the winter sea may seem to be, it has absorbed some of the warmth of summer and it holds this warmth for longer than the land, so that frosts on the coastline are much rarer and less severe than those inland. Also, the sheerness of the cliff wall excludes sheep, rabbits and other grazers, so that plants which are unable to tolerate grazing may secure little havens. And then just above the bare rock faces there may be a narrow cordon sanitaire between the world of rock and the world of man in which a strip of botanical excellence may survive. Here the air is still too salty for trees to endure, while the terrain is too risky for farming operations, and in this narrow setting a myriad of plants which have been evicted from the arenas of agriculture may make their last stands.

Amongst the humblest of the plant colonists of the cliffs are the lichens. They are quite a prominent part of the cliff palette of colours – yet are almost invariably overlooked. They are numbered with the hardiest of coastal lifeforms, though the extent of this varies and is reflected in the colours which the lichens display. Least resilient are the grey-toned lichens, exemplified by the pale, tufted fronds of the sea ivory. Below this grey zone there is a broad band of orange-coloured lichens composed of four main species, and these are all lichens which will tolerate regular splashing by the salty surf. Finally, there is a black zone of lichens which resemble algae or patches of tar and which are able to withstand submersion by the sea each time that the tides come in. In spite of their hardy constitutions, however, these lichens are unable to survive oil spillages or the chemical agents which were used to disperse the oil slicks, so that for many years after the *Torrey Canyon* disaster lichens were missing from a 320-km (200-mile) stretch of the Cornish coast. Lichens are the dominant plant of the cliff-foot zone; some belong to common inland species and others, like those of the black zone, are entirely coastal specialists.

Despite the unique qualities of the sea-cliff habitat, cliffs have not tended to acquire their own exclusive plant species. Rather, they tend to be 'discovered' and exploited by members of plant communities which flourish in other kinds of setting. The dock, for example, is known and detested by gardeners, and legends abound of its ability to survive the most frantic assaults with spade and scythe. It is also more tolerant of guano-polluted soil than most other plants, apart from a few specialised lichens. The shortage of exclusive cliff specialists has allowed the available niches to be colonised by opportunistic plants from elsewhere, and their presence on different parts of the cliff depends, to some degree, on their respective abilities to tolerate air laden with salt spray.

It is a remarkable, if not entirely explicable, fact that an important selection of the vegetables in daily use result from the cultivation of coastal plants. The list includes kale, Brussels sprouts, cauliflower, cabbage and the root crops, such as mangolds, beetroot and sugar-beet, which have been developed from the sea beet. In addition, there are herbs, such as lovage and alexanders. The wild cabbage bears little obvious resemblance to its cultivated cousins. It is an erect plant with rather leathery, dark green leaves and the yellow, four-petalled flowers are carried along an upright stem. Sea beet is even less obviously a forbear of cultivated vegetables, having glossy spear-head shaped leaves and stems clad in minute greenish flowers. Rock samphire is an edible plant which is much more widely distributed than the wild cabbage of the southern and Welsh shores. The yellow flowers are carried in an umbel above the small, fleshy leaves. Golden samphire, another plant which is found on both cliffs and shingle beaches, is not related to the rock samphire, and the yellow, daisy-like flowers are a clue to its kinship with the dainty inulas grown in gardens. In spite of the usefulness of these plants, neither they nor the clumps of weeds which thrive in the guano-enriched soils near the bird colonies can be regarded as spectacular adornments to the landscape. There are, however, a few extremely attractive cliff-dwelling plants.

Of these, the most familiar must be the thrift, with its pink inflorescences carried like pompoms above its slender, low-growing, blue-green leaves. Thrift was portrayed on the reverse of the pre-decimalisation threepenny-bit, though whilst it may have come to symbolise thrift, its name arose from its ability to thrive and remain green throughout the year. With its tolerance of high salt levels and its roots which probe deeply through rock crevices in search of water, the thrift is well adapted for its life on cliffs, shingle beaches and mountains.

Another eye-catching pink plant of the cliffs that has ingratiated itself with many gardeners is the tree mallow, which displays its dark-centred, hollyhock-like flowers on a perennial shrub which may grow up to 3 m (9 feet) tall. A smaller species of tree mallow grows in Cornwall and the Isle of Scilly.

Yet another plant found on cliffs which has secured a niche in many gardens is the little spring squill, with its intensely blue flowers, a close relation of the popular white star of Bethlehem plant. The spring squill may be found growing on dry, grassy shelves on northern and western cliffs, while on shaded ledges the bluebell, normally a plant of the woodlands, can be a most unexpected complement to the scene.

The white flowers of the sea campion resemble those of the bladder campion, and in both plants the sepals are fused to form a bladder-like tube at the base of the flower. This form was evolved to assist pollination, with bees being obliged to bumble around the flower head as they strove to reach the nectar at the base of the tube. However, some bees have learned to undermine the design by biting through the tube and sucking out the nectar. Other characteristic plants of the cliffs include English stonecrop, rock sea spurry, buck's horn plantain, common scurvy grass, sea plantain, lovage and sea spleenwort.

On the cliff tops, where there is a deeper development of soil, but also immunity from most agricultural operations, a vibrant number of plants may develop. Many are refugees from inland communities evicted by farming, so that the range of types which may be found is very wide. Scores of attractive flowering plants are among them; favourites of the author's include the abundance of wild orchids above the cliffs on Skye, primroses growing in profusion in cliff-top pastures in north Cornwall and the clumps of sheep's bit growing at the top of some of the Dyfed (Pembrokeshire) cliffs. While the cliff tops may provide a haven, the environment is not entirely welcoming; salt spray can still be a problem, rabbits graze and burrow, while the tunnels of puffins and shearwaters can drain the soil so thoroughly that only the deep roots of the thrift may be able to tap a source of moisture.

Cliff tops are also amongst the very best places at which to search for butterflies and moths. This is partly to do with the survival there of so many wild flowers, but other factors are also involved. Some insects found there have been exterminated in the agricultural districts; some are existing on the northern margins of their ranges and depend upon the winter warmth and basking slopes of the south coastal setting, while others are migrants making their landfall in Britain.

Several of our rarest breeding butterflies have their last refuges

The rare Glanville fritillary

at or close to the coast. Once found as far north as Yorkshire, the Glanville fritillary is found now only on the Isle of Wight, and Britain lies on the northern fringe of its range. With its white-edged wings, which are a mosaic of amber and brown in the fashion of the fritillaries, this butterfly loves the sun-warmed grassy slopes of the cliff tops. It takes nectar from yellow-flowered plants, such as the vetches and trefoils which favour the chalky soils, and lays its eggs on the undersides of the leaves of the sea plantain and ribwort plantain. Two rare members of the rather moth-like skipper group of butterflies, the Essex skipper and the Lulworth skipper, are also associated with coastal footholds. Skippers, which skip or dart from flower to flower, are the liveliest members of the butterfly dynasty, and though small and rather drab they are aggressive towards other insects which trespass upon their chosen territories. The Essex skipper resembles other British skippers so closely that it was only identified in 1888. But it was found to be unusual in that it overwinters as an egg rather than as a caterpillar – a fact which later helped it to survive the coastal flooding in 1953 which inundated its most important breeding grounds. Though found in many parts of the south-east and East Anglia, the Essex skipper is most common along the shores of the Thames estuary. The Lulworth skipper has a much more restricted distribution and is never found more than a few miles from Lulworth Cove. Its caterpillars feed on two types of grass found in this locality, the couch grass and the chalk false brome, and the adults live their brief lives amongst the ragwort, marjoram, fleabane, vetch and thistles of the warm, south-facing cliff tops.

If the resident skippers are a rather dull and dusty-looking tribe, most of the immigrant butterflies which flutter down to our cliffs are spectacularly colourful. Of these the most familiar must be the red admiral. Fast-flying and territorial, the butterflies fly over from the continent from May onwards and then lay the eggs which give rise to a summer, resident-born generation of red admirals. These large red, black and white butterflies were formerly known as 'aldermen', on account of their colourful garb; the modern name is a corruption of another old name for the butterfly, the 'admirable'. Another eye-catching migrant which may make its first landfall on cliffs is the painted lady. Its rather pointed wings are marked in amber and black and have white markings on their black tips. Despite their delicate appearance, these butterflies make remarkable migration flights, sometimes covering 1,130 km (700 miles). They arrive in late spring from their winter homes in North Africa and south-western Europe after flights which may have lasted for a hundred hours. The numbers which arrive in Britain are controlled by a range of factors, such as wind and weather; in some years painted ladies are scarce and in others they are relatively common. Although eggs, caterpillars and adults all perish with the onset of the British winter, the immigrants breed here to create a generation of painted ladies which can be seen in early autumn.

Two migrants which are occasionally seen around the British coast, the monarch and the Camberwell beauty, are rare, large and spectacular. With a wingspan 10 cm (4 inches), the monarch is the largest butterfly which may be found in Britain. The wings are orange-veined in black and hemmed in black spotted with white and the black body of the butterfly is also dotted with white. The migration flights of the painted lady pale into insignificance when compared to those of the monarch, for each autumn monarchs fly from their summer homes in Canada and the north of the USA to communal wintering places in the south, many of them in Mexico. The distances covered can be as far as 2,500 km (1,500 miles). From time to time flocks of monarchs are swept eastwards and carried right across the Atlantic, and the butterflies which have survived the traumas make landfalls in Ireland or the west of Scotland, England and Wales. However, there is nothing here to permit a resident population of monarchs to develop, for its caterpillars must eat the milkweed plant which does not grow in

The clouded yellow is a migrant which is most likely to be glimpsed at coastal sites

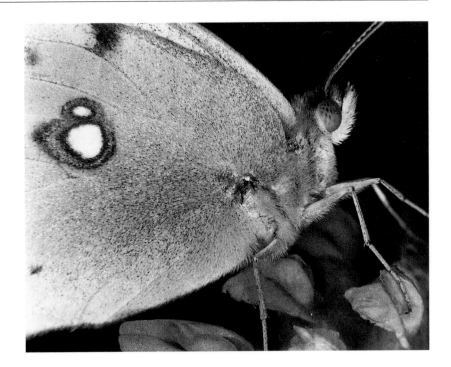

Britain away from botanical collections. In some years there may be no reliable reports of monarchs in Britain, but in others there can be a hundred or more sightings. The butterflies are most likely to be reported at the western extremities of Britain, in the Isles of Scilly or Cornwall.

In contrast, the Camberwell beauty, as a migrant from Scandinavia, is more likely to be seen on east- and north-facing coasts. This is another striking butterfly; the deep wine-coloured wings have an inner border of light-blue dots on a black ground and an outer border of pale cream. Some of these butterflies appear to make the North Sea crossing in spring while others may arrive, still deep in hibernation, amongst cargoes of softwood timber shipped to east coast ports. In any event the total arriving is small and the butterfly was not identified in England until 1748, when it was named after what was then a south London village lying close to the willow trees where it was spotted. Riverside willows and orchards growing near the south-east coasts are the most likely places for the discovery of this rare visitor.

The clouded yellow butterfly is a much more reliable visitor, but there are also two closely related species of clouded yellow which are more infrequent arrivals. The clouded yellow is a butterfly of medium size with orange-yellow wings which, when open, display a broad border of black. It arrives in late spring from southern Europe, where it is common and prolific, and large influxes of clouded yellows may be found in Britain when the continental population becomes swollen and the butterflies are forced to expand their range. These restless butterflies may be seen around any British coast, and they also arrive in all parts of the interior, feeding on leguminous plants like vetches, lucerne, trefoil, and also on thistles and marjoram. The first arrivals lay eggs which give rise to a summer, home-grown generation, but all stages of the insect perish as the weather turns cool and wet in autumn. As its name suggests, the pale clouded yellow lacks the strong colouration of its cousin, and the female of this species is white and recognised by a yellow wing spot and the row of white spots on the black wing border. The migrations of the pale clouded yellow are much more erratic and it is seldom found far from the southern coastal strip, even though it favours the same meadow settings and food plants. Again, a late summer generation is produced and there is a slight chance that their offspring may survive through a mild winter. Berger's clouded yellow is visually almost indistinguishable from this butterfly, although the male has a stronger, lemony colouration and the caterpillar has different markings and is normally found on horseshoe vetch. The migrant which, on account of its rarity and unremarkable appearance, is least likely to be spotted is the Bath white, a rare visitor to the south coast of England, which is white with a black marbling around the tips and edges of the wings.

To our eyes the cliffs of Britain form environments which are often harsh and uninviting, but to some specialised, exhausted or hard-pressed members of the plant and animal kingdoms they can exist as havens. The cliffs offer fascination in many forms, but they also embody a danger which can be underestimated during the quests which fascination spawns. The convex slopes of the cliff top will often mask the sheerness of the rock face which lies just a few feet below, and the damp turf and sharply increasing gradients here increase the risks of slipping. Sometimes the dangers of the vegetated cliff top zone are not obvious, as when a layer of greasy and unstable boulder clay forms a treacherous capping to hard rock cliffs, or when rabbits or burrowing birds have destabilised the earth of the cliff top. Cliffs can also be dangerous when viewed from a position too close to their foot, for all rock faces are actively eroding – and one can never quite know when rocks are ready to fall.

We have all collected sea shells and peered into the fascinating miniature world of the rock pool, and so we know that many beaches are vibrant with life. On the other hand, anyone who had never explored a coast might have every reason to regard beaches as places which should be dead and hostile to life. For some of the time they are exposed to the sky and to hordes of scavenging seabirds, while every few hours they are submerged and prone to attack by angry waves which plunge and scour. Adaptation has been the key to survival; the lower levels of the shore support a wealth of plants and animals, but the further one moves landwards on a rocky shoreline then the more rigorous and demanding the environment becomes, and the more organisms must become specialised in order to survive. Perpetually engaged in an open conflict with the sea, the rocky shorelines would seem to be more hostile to life than soft, sandy beaches. In fact the reverse is the case, for the sands shift and dry and offer no shelter or hiding places on their surface. Neither do they provide surfaces and anchorages where plants and animals can become attached. The shingle beach is the least inviting habitat, for any plant or creature attempting to make its home there may soon become crushed as the waves churn the pebbles in a maelstrom of chipping, clashing and grinding.

Although holidaymakers and most forms of coastal life disagree about the attractions of the sandy beaches, there is a fairly general consensus in the desire to avoid beaches consisting of black mud. The nature of the particles which make up the beach has an enormous influence upon the animal life which is supported. At one extreme these particles are fist-sized pebbles, and we have seen that shingle beaches are not inviting abodes. While the sand grains on a particular beach will tend to have a fairly uniform size, this grain size will vary greatly from beach to beach. Large grains have large spaces between them, so that on a beach of coarse sands the water will drain away quickly as the tide recedes, and most lifeforms will find it hard to survive as their habitat dries out. However, where the grains are finer then water is retained in the spaces between them, and beneath the barren surface of the beach there can be a great deal of burrowing activity going on. As the grains become finer still, the beach is composed of mud rather than sand; the burrowing creatures become less numerous but bacteria increase. When the muds are exposed to the heat of the sun at low tide, and when plant and animal remains accumulate in hollows, the bacterial action becomes high, and all the oxygen stored in the water between the grains is consumed. Then the muds give off a foul smell and iron sulphide from the bacterial activity accumulates to turn the muds black.

Very few animals have achieved the adaptations which are necessary for survival in this oxygen-less or 'anaerobic' world. But it soon becomes apparent that this barren and tainted setting is not entirely lifeless, for there is ample evidence of the lob-worm or lug-worm from the casts on the surface and the fishermen out digging for bait. Almost as thick as a finger and around 22 cm (9 inches) long, the lug-worm inhabits a somewhat U-shaped tunnel in mud or sand, and the sides of this are consolidated with mucus excreted by the worm. The tunnel has two fairly vertical shafts which are linked by a near-horizontal gallery in which the worm lives. It moves back and forth in this gallery, using small bristles on its body to grip the sides of the tunnel. When feeding, its head is at the base of one shaft and the constant intake of mud or sand causes a depression to form where this 'head shaft' reaches the surface. Within its tunnel, the worm continually makes waves of contraction which pass along its body to create a current in the surrounding water. This current passes up the head shaft, loosening sand and oxygenating what might otherwise be an anaerobic setting. The loosened grains of mud or sand which fall down the head shaft then pass through the body of the lob-worm, any organic foods which they contain are extracted, and the grains are then excreted through the tail shaft of the tunnel to form the distinctive worm casts. Fishermen can obtain their bait by digging between the head shaft depressions and the casts which mark the tail shafts to catch the worms in their galleries. The lob-worms seldom leave their galleries, but each tide renews the food supply available above the head shaft. They survive in hostile settings by creating currents in the way described, by having a rich endowment of red blood, which serves as an oxygen store, and by extending their tails to the surface of the mud to trap bubbles of air which are then passed to the feathery gills carried on the middle section of the body. Such adaptations are essential at times when the tide is out and the tunnel filled with stagnant water.

Muddy shores are associated with very slight gradients, for if the slopes were steeper then the fine-grained particles would all be swept away. In spite of the hardships of life here there are also certain advantages. The muds retain moisture in the tiny spaces between the particles, so that the surfaces of mud flats do not dry out between tides. They also provide a better, firmer medium for home-making than do the shifting sands.

Burrowing removes many of the hardships which would be associated with life on the surface of a muddy or sandy beach. Rainfall at low tide seldom affects conditions more than a few centimetres below the surface, so that the salinity, which is essential to marine life, is preserved. Neither does the heat from the sun inflict an intolerable rise in temperature upon an animal safely insulated in the depths of its burrow. Even the shifting and scouring of the sea seldom affects much more than the uppermost centimetres of mud and sand, though 1 m (1 yard) or more of sand and all the life it contains can be shifted during a severe storm.

The sand-mason is a common tube-worm found on the lower levels of sandy beaches. It is around 22 cm (9 inches) long, with branched gills and long tentacles around its head. When the water is high, this head is exposed, and food, derived from decaying seaweed, and sand grains are gathered by the waving tentacles. The worm inhabits a flexible tube of sand grains which are bound by a matrix of mucus, and while the beachcomber may never catch sight of the sand-masons themselves, there will be abundant evidence of their presence, for the ends of these long sand tubes, which project about 3 cm (1 inch) above the surface of the sand, can be seen at low tide. Sandy and muddy shores are home to a variety of other tube-worms, some of them, like the peacock worm, being very common. This worm builds and inhabits a tube of mud which is around 30 cm (1 foot) long, and which has its sunken end attached to stones. When the beach is under water the worm emerges from its tube and gathers food in its waving tentacles. Peacock worms can gather together in large numbers, and when feeding with their tentacles outspread they resemble a miniature forest of swaying palm trees. This is a colourful creature with an olive, violet and orange body and red, brown and purple banded tentacles.

Some molluscs also live in burrows in the mud. The sand gaper is known as a clam in North America, where it is a popular food. It has an oval brown or grey shell which is around 12 cm (5 inches) long and half this in width. In early life it is a mobile shellfish, but later it adapts to a life of being buried around a foot or more beneath the surface of the mud. As the gaper grows and the tube-like siphon extending up to the surface elongates, so the creature burrows more deeply. The opening of the siphon is fringed in tiny tentacles, and it collects plankton and other fragments of food from the waters just above the mud surface. The sand gaper is common in sand and mud while another gaper, the blunt gaper, is a little smaller but is able to make its home in very stiff muds.

While these gapers lead very sedentary lives within the firm, moist worlds of the mud flats, razor-shells are associated with sandy beaches and very active burrowing abilities. Their shells, shaped like the old cut-throat razors, are unmistakable and frequently found. There are two common types, one having a slightly more curved shell than the other. The elongated form of the shell offers little resistance, so that these animals are capable of surprisingly rapid movement. Around high tide, the razor-shells come close to the surface of the sand and project their siphons into the water above to gather food, but as the sea retreats the animals burrow into the lower, saturated layers. They remain sensitive to movements above, and can usually burrow away more swiftly than a man can dig. The shell is hinged, allowing a 'foot' to protrude and the contractions in the muscles of this foot and those of the shell create a sort of pumping motion which flushes away the sand and drives the animal downwards. Though common, razor-shells are also localised, and most inhabit the muddier types of sand and live in the zone of the low watermark.

Yet another hardship for marine life occurs in the muds of the upper reaches of estuaries, where the salinity levels are greatly diluted by the influx of fresh river water. Here, too, the muds may be very fine, and this makes it difficult for animals adjusted to life in more sandy surroundings to burrow or move, whilst the mist of fine particles will tend to block their feeding and breathing apendages. One mollusc which can flourish in such testing habitats is the peppery furrow shell. The somewhat rounded shell is up to 5 cm (2 inches) in length, grey or yellowish in colour and very flattened. The animal does not move about very much, but burrows to a depth of up to 22 cm (9 inches) into the estuarine muds and extends its siphon into the food-laden waters. Although relatively few species are able to cope with the special difficulties of estuarine life, there are rich pickings for those which can. In places ten of these peppery furrow shells can be found in each 0.1 m² (square foot) of mud on the estuary bed. The animal itself, however, is seldom seen, although those who walk across the mud flats at low tide may see the little star-shaped imprints in the mud which were left by the siphons of these animals as they waved in different directions in search of food. Cockles are more adaptable than most other molluscs and may be found within the

The shelduck has a beak designed for scooping and filtering food from the mud-flats

mud, while the surface of the muddy beach may be home to mussels, shore crabs and periwinkles.

Food of different types can be found at different levels on the beach, and so that they do not all compete for the same source; the birds which exploit beach resources have developed in ways which allow different species to hunt for different prey. Ducks, notably the shelduck, do not have bills designed for probing deeply into the muds and silts but for shovelling and filtering the surface deposits. It is here that small snails, like the scavenger, hydrobia, can be found. Gulls have bills designed for general purpose scavenging, and while they cannot dig for prey, they will take shellfish, like mussels, from the surface of the beach, fly up and drop them on rocks to break the shells, and then devour the contents. A more specialised feeder on surface resources is the turnstone. Its rather short bill is unusual in having a slightly upward curve, which makes it ideal for turning over stones

Though equally at home in the rough pastures of the moorland margins, the curlew, with its long legs and probing beak, is well-equipped for life as a coastal wader

to discover any small crabs which may be lurking beneath them.

The variations in design which help the different species to secure their own niches in the great coastal restaurant concern legs as well as bills. Curlews, whimbrels and godwits have long legs which allow them to wade, while short-legged birds, such as stints and dunlins, are confined to the shore. With its very long, down-curving bill the curlew is able to probe the mud sufficiently deeply to reach lug-worms. The bar-tailed godwit has quite long legs and a longish straight beak and can wade and probe for various large molluscs; the redshank has fairly long legs but a shorter beak and can probe deeply enough to reach molluscs, like the Baltic tellin, which is common in estuaries with a low salinity, as well as marine worms. The dunlin is less well endowed in the legs and bill departments and, like the ringed plover and stint, its hunting activities are confined to the two or three surface centimetres of the beach and mud flat. Phalaropes have developed their own peculiar feeding techniques, for they bob on the surface of shallow waters, periodically spinning round to swirl up tiny creatures from the water below. In the case of the rare avocet, the differences in build prevent competition between the adults and the immature birds. The adults have the long legs necessary for wading and long, upturned bills which are swept back and forth in search of shrimps, larvae and insects. The youngsters, however, have shorter, straighter bills and are better equipped to hunt for beetles and fly larvae in shallower waters.

The adaptations to reduce competition which are so obvious in the bird kingdom are replicated amongst the other categories of beach life. There is not just one common form of shellfish but many, each one slightly different in its way of life and feeding habits. Many of the creatures of the sandy beaches and mud flats are filter feeders, equipped to sieve plankton from the sea water at high tide. Others are 'deposit feeders', which ingest large quantities of mud and strain out the nutritious morsels. And there are also predators, like the ragworm, a burrowing carnivore, the snail-like necklace shell, which drills through the shells of tellins, and the starfish, as well as various scavengers.

While the birds of the beach have their own obvious methods of escape and cannot afford to be too concerned about concealment, most of the beach creatures are adapted to seek safety by burrowing. As we have seen, the razor-shells are so finely adapted for escape that they can usually burrow more swiftly than a man can dig. Cockles move through the sand in a fashion which is popular in the shellfish world; they extend a 'foot', and the end of this foot then expands and gains a purchase in the surrounding medium and the rest of the cockle's body is then drawn towards this anchor. Scallops, however, are something of an exception, for instead of tunnelling, they flee their predators by flapping their shells in a sort of underwater flight and assist their escape by ejecting a jet of water as a means of propulsion.

Creatures which depend on burrowing into sands and muds or which seek to live on the wave-lapped surface of the beach have developed body forms which offer the least resistance to burrowing or to rushing water. Such forms include the slender cylindrical bodies of the worms, the streamlined shells of the razor-shells and the flattened, pocket-watch lines of many molluscs. Several of the more common fish of the beach also have extremely flattened forms, which are exploited mainly for camouflage since they become almost invisible when settled on the seabed under a dusting of sand.

Crabs have also developed a flattened form, allowing them to slip beneath the sands and to reduce their water resistance. There are many species of crab which fully exploit the burrowing mode of life, but only one example, the masked crab, is found in British waters. It uses its legs to dig and to pull its body down into the sand and then its two antennae fit together to create a breathing tube which sucks down freshwater into its gills. It may be found on beaches, but it prefers to live below the low watermark. It is active as a scavenger at night, but during the daytime it lies concealed and buried from predators, such as the skate, with only the tip of its breathing tube visible at the surface.

Although they are designed in a completely different manner, shrimps are also burrowers. They do this by shuffling sand away with their feet, and then beating it away with their 'tails'. When their bodies are nearly concealed, the long antennae are used to sweep grains over the remaining portions – so that only two tiny branches on the antennae remain exposed to sense for food. Shrimps have an additional means of concealment, for they have pigment cells which allow their body tone to be adjusted to match the surrounding sand or mud. Like the masked crab, shrimps are nocturnal; they emerge from the surface of the sand to forage at night, when they take a remarkably wide range of plant and animal foods. When hunting, they do not tend to swim, but rather wander across the surface of the submerged beach on their rear-most legs, while feeling for food with their forelegs. They are one of the most successful of the creatures of the beach and are able to tolerate variations in temperatures and the changing levels of salinity associated with estuary life.

Prawns are larger and come in several species. They are not essentially creatures of the beach, instead they prefer to winter in offshore waters and colonise the rock pool zone as the temperature rises in spring. They have five pairs of legs and use the nippers on the first two pairs for scavenging, while the remaining legs are employed in walking. Prawns are more ready to swim than are shrimps; they beat the water with the swimming appendages on the underside of their bodies and they can also make a rapid departure from danger by rapidly bending their bodies and so rushing backwards through the water.

Shrimps form the diet of one of the few true beach fish. The weaver fish is an inconspicuous grey creature, about 15 cm (6 inches) in length, which also employs burrowing tactics so that it can lurk with only a fraction of its upper surface exposed, whilst appraising its surroundings through bulbous eyes which are conveniently placed high and forward on the head. It lives amongst the shrimp-infested sands and presents a real hazard to bare-footed shrimpers, for the long, black back fin is armed with poisonous spines which can inflict a painful, but not fatal, sting even after the fish is dead. The greater weaver fish is three times as long as its smaller cousin, but is less likely to be encountered by paddlers, since it inhabits deeper waters.

A variety of fish, such as sole and dabs, are attracted to the tidal zone to prey upon the rich populations of worms, but the number of resident species is much smaller than that of the high tide visitors. Two forms of sand eel are common, one around 20 cm (8 inches) long and another of twice this length. These are not true eels, but elongated fish which have developed a burrowing habit for defence. They have evolved projecting, spade-like lower jaws, slender bodies and narrow fins to assist their entry into the sands. This quest for safety is fully justified, for sand eels are a favourite prey for porpoises as well as for seabirds, such as terns and puffins. Shoaling is another defensive strategy, and sand eels are most likely to be glimpsed in low water as darting needles of silver, their flashing side stripes being more visible than their green backs.

Rocky shores offer many more opportunities to life than do the sandy beaches, and a wide variety of different plants and animals have evolved to exploit these turbulent and restricted habitats. Rock and rock pool settings are generally found where the sea is actively eroding the adjacent cliffs, and where its waters tow away the debris and beach materials to prevent the hollows in the wave-cut platform being choked with sand. The best potential for rich and varied rock pool life is found where the coast is formed by dipping beds of layered sedimentary rock, with each bed forming a miniature scarp to trap water from the retreating tide. But when these ideal conditions are not met, hollows for pools can be gouged as the slightly softer sections of rock are scoured more deeply, and where pebbles and boulders rolling in the waves grind little pits in the surface of the platform.

The inter-tidal zone is a very restricted habitat, and so the competition for niches is intense. As a result, some of the would-be denizens of the rock pool zone have been obliged to adapt to living on the hostile margins of the zone, in places which are exposed for much of the day. Although some creatures of the open sea find themselves trapped in rock pools by the retreating

tide, most of the life-forms present are specially tailored for exist-ence in a cramped little world which is both rich and challenging. The challenges arise from the great variability in the conditions which have to be confronted. The state of the water in a rock pool which the tide has detached from the great reservoir of the ocean may fluctuate greatly, for while the pool may not dry up, the summer sun will warm the waters to Mediterranean levels, while evaporation causes a considerable rise in their salinity. On the other hand, intense winter cold can cause the surface to ice over, and heavy rain streaming into the pool will lower the levels of salinity. The changes created by the occupants of the pool are also important, for carbon dioxide released by the plants at night can raise the acidity of the waters to levels which may become intoler-able before the tide brings its sudden refreshment. Most of the hardships mentioned are more extreme in small pools than in large ones, but each pool has a strange existence, being a part of

A green seaweed which tolerates the steady trickle of fresh water emerging from the cliffs

the sea for one period of the day, and an isolated aquarium for another.

Although the rocks of the cliff foot provide attachments for the seaweeds which are lacking on the sand and muddy beaches, only a few of these plants are able to survive on the rocks around the high watermark. The fronds of seaweeds of the Enteromorpha family can variously be found in situations of freshened and brackish water, and these and other green seaweeds can survive in the higher tiers of pools. Brown seaweeds have evolved in different ways to colonise the different levels of the shore. Kelp has a strong but pliable stem, which allows the plant to sway with the waves which churn the waters at the lower levels of the shore. On the middle level of the shore may be found the knotted wrack and the bladder wrack. Both these seaweeds are furnished with gas-filled bladders which help them to float with their fronds well spread in the strong currents of the tidal zone, the bladder wrack having the shorter, stronger fronds and being better able to withstand the beating waves on exposed shores.

Higher on the beach the problem is not so much that of surviving in swirling currents but of withstanding the drought at low tide. Two other brown seaweeds, the channelled wrack and the spiral wrack, have adapted to meet this challenge. In the case of the former, the fronds curl to enclose a channel in which water may be retained, and this wrack also resists desiccation by having a high oil content. Both these wracks grow in much slower and more compact manners than do their cousins in the pools below. They may live for three-quarters of the time exposed to the sky and may lose up to two-thirds of their water content in the period between tides. At such times, they appear shrivelled, blackened and dead – but they will quickly absorb water and swell, becoming plastic rather than brittle and so be able to sway with the current.

Weeds such as these provide the animals of the rock pools with morsels of food from broken fronds, but no less important is the shelter which they offer. Without the protection of the swaying submarine forests there would be few hiding places, while most of the living contents of the pools would be swept away in the rushing waters.

Several shellfish do not need this kind of protection, and they survive the rigours of pounding and desiccation by clasping tightly to rocks. They are equipped with shells which allow a tight seal to be achieved when their flat, circular 'feet' cling to rocks so that water is retained within the shell until the sea returns. These

shells are designed in flattened, conical forms which maximise the surface area available for clasping while minimising the resistance to the waves. Research has shown that limpets living on exposed rock tend to develop taller, narrower shells than those which live out their lives in rock pools. Limpets have become synonymous with clinging, and the stronger the forces tugging at these animals then the more strongly they will cling. At low tide the limpet's gills breath in water which is trapped in a groove running around the inner margin of the shell, and a watertight seal is achieved by grinding the rock of the anchorage point with the shell, and vice versa, until a perfect fit is achieved. This precisely tailored anchorage becomes the home base for journeys of up to 1 m (1 yard) into the surrounding feeding grounds, where the limpets browse on algae covering the rocks around. This browsing has an enormous effect upon the landscape of the rocky shore, for it keeps large

Limpets and barnacles are common in most rock pools

Mussels crammed tightly together

areas free of seaweed. Limpets can be found in densities of up to 150 per square metre and can exert an enormous control over the colonisation of the shore by algae.

Barnacles are not molluscs but crustaceans, and they have developed a rather different attachment technique. They are the commonest of shoreline creatures, and exist in a number of different species which are adapted for life on different levels of the rocky shore. Barnacle larvae drift freely in the water until they 'select' a place for attachment. Then the feelers on the front of the head produce a cement which bonds the animal to a rock and its body undergoes a complicated series of changes. It becomes encased in six limy plates which are hinged in such a way that the shell becomes tightly sealed at low tide, but when the barnacle is covered by water these plates open and six feathery appendages emerge and are used to waft particles of food into the animal's mouth. Once secured to its rock, the barnacle will live for between three and six years.

Mussels, which can often be found in vast numbers from the middle shore seawards, employ a different method of attachment and are bonded to rocks by short threads formed of a sticky fluid which the animal secretes. These threads radiate so that they can take the strain of currents pushing and pulling in any direction, while the body of the animal can swing around so that its sharp end faces the rushing water to exploit the streamlining of the narrow, oval shell. Mussels are also able to cope with the deposition of sand and mud upon the seabed, for they produce new, longer threads which allow the creature to rise above its attachment and maintain a position on the surface. The hinged blue-black shell remains tightly closed when the mussel is exposed, but as the sea returns it opens, allowing the animal to feed and breath by straining plankton-rich water through its gills. The saddle oyster cements its shell to stones near the low watermark, and it does so in such a way that its silvery shell clings closely to the contours of the boulder to offer the least resistance to the waves.

There are other creatures, like the members of the piddock family, which do not gain security by clasping or bonding, but by drilling refuges into the rocks of the shore. Their slender shells are extremely hard and are armed with saw-like teeth. Contractions of the body of the piddock create a rasping action as these teeth are brought to bear on the rock; meanwhile, the animal slowly rotates its position so that a circular tunnel is drilled.

There are others still which rely neither upon attachment nor upon burrowing, but which are prepared to be rolled and buffeted by the waves if the circumstances arise. The most obvious of these are the periwinkles, with their familiar coiled snail shells. These shells are almost spherical and are very strong; when the periwinkles find themselves adrift in the current they seal the openings of their shells with horny plates which they carry on their 'feet'. And when the animals are left high and dry they attach themselves to rocks by these feet and secrete a mucus which lightly bonds the edges of their shells to these rocks, to prevent desiccation. While many of the inhabitants of the rock pool are creatures which have learned to survive the periodic retreat of the open sea, the periwinkles are more fully adapted to life on the land. Although the common periwinkle can be found on all levels of the tidal zone down to the low watermark, the small periwinkle is quite at home in the uppermost zone which is only splashed by the waves at high tide. There it can graze on lichens and seek protection in rock crevices when the waves pound the cliff base. However, it is not truly a land animal, for it still reproduces by liberating its spawn into the sea. Top shells, with their more conical forms, are also equipped to withstand the rigours of being swept about in the currents of the shore. The largest of these is the common or painted top shell with a conical shell about 2 cm (1 inch) high and broad, and usually yellow or pink with red streaks, found on the lower shore.

Just like the worlds of the veldt or the Arctic tundra, that of the rock pool has its herbivores and its predators. Periwinkles, top shells and limpets browse upon the algae which carpets the surrounding rocks, but they are always at risk from carnivorous molluscs, as are the barnacles and mussels. The dog whelk preys upon all these creatures. The tip of its proboscis is toothed, allowing the dog whelk to drill through the shells of its victims, this process being assisted by the secretion of acid to soften the limy armour. Once the shell has been perforated, the dog whelk is able to insert its proboscis and devour the prey within its home, though in the case of the barnacle it is thought that a poison is injected, causing the creature to relax the muscles which secure its armour. The diet favoured by a particular dog whelk is evident from the colour of its shell, the barnacle eaters being white whilst those which have fed on mussels are of a dark brownish or mauveish hue. Dog whelks are scarcely larger than periwinkles and are not to be confused with the edible whelks, owners of the largest coiled shells which can be found on our beaches. The edible whelks, however, live well to seaward of the coastal strip and are not equipped to survive exposure, so that the shells which are found on the beach are the washed-up relics of animals which died out on the seabed.

Whelk shells form the eventual homes of hermit crabs, though the developing crabs adopt cosier homes in the shells of smaller molluscs, such as periwinkles and dog whelks. While other crabs and lobsters rely on their own home-grown armour for protection, the hermit crab, with its relatively soft body, exploits the tougher shell of the whelk – at the price of having to drag its heavy home around with it as it forages. With its superior protection, however, the hermit crab is well equipped for life on the rocky shore, where it faces severe buffeting by the waves. The rear sections of the abdomen clasp tightly to the inner structures of the shell, while the crab's armoured claws can be arranged to block the door to the

home. One disadvantage of this way of life is that the shell cannot grow with the crab, so, like other home owners who move on to better things, the hermit crab must periodically go house-hunting.

The relationship with the whelk is not a mutually advantageous or 'symbiotic' one, since the whelks which provided the shells were long since deceased when the crabs moved in. But the hermit crab does enjoy such relationships with other forms of rock pool life. Of these, the most notable are with the sea anemones, which find anchorages upon the whelk shell and are given mobility by its tenant. As the hermit crab scavenges, the resident anemones lower their tentacles to capture morsels of food swept up by the animal, and in return their ability to sting unwelcome intruders endows the crab with an additional form of protection. A more curious association is shared with a form of ragworm which inhabits the same shell and wriggles around above the upper surface of the crab. It enjoys the same protection and mobility and may repay its debts by helping to keep the home fresh and clean. In fact the hermit crab and its home constitute a little community, for the exterior of the shell may harbour barnacles, sponges and hydroids and the crab itself is exploited by a parasitic barnacle.

A close-up view of the head of the shore crab

Many other types of crab inhabit our shores. Contrary to popular belief, the small specimens so often found on beaches and in rock pools are unlikely to be the young offspring of the edible crabs which are sold at the booths by the beach. These large crabs spawn offshore in the winter, and although immature individuals may be found around the low watermark in summer, edible crabs favour the deeper waters beyond the tidal zone. The crab which is most frequently encountered on our beaches is the little common shore crab, which is able to flourish in a broad spectrum of conditions and which can be found throughout the whole rock pool zone. In addition to the two types of hermit crab, there are almost twenty other types of crab to be found in British waters, and almost all of these are associated with the lower sections of the shore, where they live under stones and amongst seaweed. Despite their fearsome appearance and the aggressive displays staged by common shore crabs and fiddler crabs when they are threatened, most crabs are not predators but scavengers and rely mainly on fragments of seaweed for food. Lobsters live in the waters beyond the tidal zone. Only in summer, when the animals tend to move into shallower waters, is there any real chance of finding a lobster in a deep pool on the lower shore. There are four types of squat lobster, which are adapted for crawling along the seabed, and also the brown rock lobster or crawfish and the edible lobster – in life not red like the boiled specimens at the fishmonger's, but a deep shade of blue.

The creature which is perhaps most closely associated with the rock pools of our memory and imagination is the sea anemone. These are not plants but soft-bodied animals which attach themselves to rocks and have bodies in the form of stocky 'stems' which are surmounted by a petal-like arrangement of waving tentacles. The mouth of the animal is at the centre of the tentacle 'flower' and the tentacles, which are armed with stinging glands, are used to paralyse and to waft and direct any small animals which stray within their reach towards this mouth.

The most commonly encountered anemone is the dark red beadlet anemone, which is frequently seen as a blob of jelly attached to a rock pool boulder. It adopts this protective form by retracting its tentacles to avoid drying out when exposed by the tide. Some other anemones, like the brightly coloured gem anemone of the south-western shores, can also resort to this means of protection, but the snakelocks anemone, with its plume of serpent-like pale green tentacles, is unable to retract and will only inhabit the deep and sheltered pools of the lower shore. The largest of the anemones is the dahlia, with its tentacles banded in shades of crimson and cream, and which prefers the parts of pools which are shaded from the sun. Closely associated with the colonies of sea anemones are the sea slugs, molluscs lacking shells, and which are hideous or beautiful according to one's point of view. They include a large number of species, such as the sea hare and the sea lemon, and several have slug-like bodies adorned with waving processes or 'papillae' and decorated in a galaxy of colours. These bizarre molluscs are able to prey upon sea anemones and they actually store the stinging cells of their victims and redeploy them in their own papillae, presumably rendering these slow-moving and unarmoured creatures immune against attack by fish.

No survey of rock pools could be complete without mentions of starfish and sea urchins. Both are 'echinoederms', creatures with radial symmetry. Sea urchins are almost spherical in form and are covered in protective spines. Their skeletons or 'tests' are made of limy plates, and while not truly external, as in the case of the crabs, they are covered in just a thin skin of living tissue. Urchins have tube feet allowing them to move slowly across the seabed, where they browse on weed-encrusted rocks, and these feet also anchor the animals firmly to rocks. The tests of deceased urchins are more frequently discovered on the beaches than the living animals, almost all of which inhabit the seaweed and boulder zone of the lower shore. The sand urchin or sea potato, however, may be found burrowing on the middle reaches of sandy beaches, where its rather heart-shaped body, which is thickly clad in soft spines, matches the buff tones of its habitat. Half a dozen or more types of sea urchin can be discovered in British waters, the most frequently encountered being the common sea urchin, which is up to 15 cm (6 inches) in diameter and has a deep red test covered with white tubercles.

Starfish are predators with appearances which are far more attractive than their eating habits. Common starfish are abundant in beds of mussels and are able to breach the defences of these seemingly impregnable creatures. The five arms are covered in tube feet, allowing the starfish to clamp itself around a mussel shell and gradually prise the shell slightly open. Then it protrudes its stomach through its tiny mouth and into the interior of the mussel shell, and digests the unfortunate creature within the walls of its own home. Like the other residents of the turbulent shoreline, the starfish is always likely to have its appendages crushed between rolling rocks or seized by passing fish. And like the crabs which are adapted to shed their claws with the minimum of resistance, starfish will readily surrender their arms and grow replacements.

Different types of starfish favour different environmental niches, many occupying the seaweed and boulder habitats, while others flourish in sand or gravel situations. All prefer the lower shore or the sea bed beyond the tidal zone, though they are often swept up by the waves and stranded in rock pools and on beaches. The common starfish may grow to reach a diameter of around 50 cm (20 inches), though most that are washed up on the shore are just 6 or 7 cm (2 or 3 inches) across. Normally it has five arms to provide it with the familiar star-shaped form, though some individuals have four arms and some six. The colour is generally a brick red, though the range of hues is from tan to violet. The common sunstar, another resident of the lower shore which may be found on sandy beaches, has ten to twelve arms and a colour range from yellow to purplish red. The common brittle star has fragile arms which are about five times as long as the creature's central disc, and these beautiful creatures may be up to 22 cm (9 inches) in diameter. Writhing movements of the spiny arms allow the brittle stars to move very quickly across the seabed. A small grey type of brittle star is the starfish most commonly found in rock pools, while most other forms are more likely to be discovered beneath stones and boulders near the low watermark.

A number of fish have become specially adapted to meet the challenges of life in the inter-tidal zone. To the extent that one can generalise, these fish tend to be small and, to our eyes, rather ugly, like bizarre variations on the bullhead of the freshwater streams. The various members of the blenny family are among the most highly adapted. They are tolerant of the harsh and fast-changing conditions of rock pool life and have soft, tapering and very slippery bodies. The shanny is less than 15 cm (6 inches) long but the eel pout can reach a length of 60 cm (2 feet). The latter is remarkable in that it does not lay spawn but gives birth to live young. The shanny has not reached this level of development, but the male keeps guard over the eggs until they hatch. Such habits are not found amongst the fish of the open ocean, but the protection of eggs and young is practised by several rock pool species, which lay far fewer eggs than most other fish but which defend their offspring as they gain a familiarity with the settings which they will inhabit. In the case of another blenny, the gunnel or butter-fish, the parents loop their bodies around their eggs to prevent them being sucked away by the shallow water currents. The butter-fish are the most tolerant of inter-tidal conditions and will survive in tiny puddles of water beneath boulders until the sea returns.

In addition to the seven species of blenny, British coastal waters harbour ten species of goby. These are small fish with frog-like eyes placed high on their heads, and they share a peculiar modification in having their pelvic fins fused to form a sucker on the undersides of their bodies. This sucker allows the goby to attach itself to rocks, and this may help the fish to remain safe and stable amongst the pounding waves and swirling currents of the tidal zone. A more effective version of the same modification is exploited by the lumpsucker, a thick-set fish up to 60 cm (2 feet) in length which comes into the rock pool zone to spawn. The male lumpsucker then guards the eggs against predators, using its very powerful sucker to retain a firm anchorage in the most stormy of conditions. The young may remain in the rock pools until they are several centimetres in length, and they too exploit their suckers in the struggles against waves and currents. Among the most peculiar of the adaptations for caring for young are those shown by the pipe-fishes, creatures with snake-like bodies and heads like those of sea-horses. The snake pipe-fish and the worm pipe-fish have their eggs 'glued' in lines to the undersides of their bodies, but in the case of the large great pipe-fish the male has a pouch, like that of a marsupial, in which the eggs are carried. After hatching, some of the young may return to this pouch for protection. Finally, there are the nest-builders, a group which includes most of those seven members of the wrasse family which are found in British waters. They lay their eggs in nests scooped in sheltered places, and later their young spend some time out at sea before returning to their rock pool habitats. The wrasses are small, brightly and variously coloured fish, and are equipped with strong teeth which allow them to crunch through the shells of crustaceans and molluscs.

Beaches of sand, mud and shingle and the rock pool zone at the foot of cliffs each constitute a distinctive and fascinating habitat, but there is another which must be mentioned which is no less distinctive or fascinating: that of the sea loch. Each sea loch is a world which consists of several quite different worlds, and each, unless defiled by human greed, supports a remarkable richness of

A loch on Orkney

life. The sea lochs of Scotland and the loughs of Ireland were created by glaciers which over-deepened existing valleys and inlets, gouging channels which are characteristically deeper to landward than at their outlets. As the tides bring water surging in over the shallow lip at the mouth of the sea loch then currents running as fast as ten knots may be recorded, and the resulting turbulence stirs up a great richness of nutrients. Within the confined world of the sea loch there are enormous contrasts. Around its mouth there may be islands formed by mounds of glacial deposits known as 'drumlins' and tidal mud-flats which provide havens and feeding grounds for ducks, geese and waders. The waters of the mouth itself abound in nourishment, but are shallow and violent – although just a short distance to landward the water becomes deep and calm in the shelter of the embracing hills.

Strangford Lough, near Belfast, is said to be the British sea loch which is the most diverse and rich in terms of its wildlife. It is only about 30 km (20 miles) long and 5 or 6 km (3 or 4 miles) wide and yet it supports more than 2,000 different species of marine life, a figure which comprises around seventy per cent of all the lifeforms known in Northern Irish waters. One-third of all the terns nesting in Ireland are to be found on the drumlins which punctuate the waters of the loch, 500 common seals breed on its shores and the vast bird population includes 15,000 pale-bellied brent geese, amounting to almost three-quarters of the west European wintering population. Recently steps have been taken to safeguard this richness, for mounting recreational pressures were being reflected in the decline in the numbers of some bird species.

The mammals of the coastal zone are few but fascinating. The otters glimpsed in northern coastal waters are identical to those which still inhabit some rivers in England and Wales. However, the chances of encountering otters on remote Scottish shores are much greater than those of seeing an otter further south. In the more populated parts of the country the justifiable fear of man has encouraged otters to adopt a nocturnal way of life, and the animals have become either rare or extinct. But along the northern shores and western sea lochs otters are relatively common and will still hunt in daylight. In Shetland, however, where otters are numerous along the island shores, deaths resulting from oil spillages have become a serious threat.

Many of the otters fish inland waters for eels, salmon, trout, sticklebacks and frogs during the spring and summer and resort to the coast in winter, where they scour the tidal zone for shellfish, crabs or injured creatures which have been stranded on the beaches. Others are permanent coastal dwellers. The animals are territorial and each male may guard a stretch of the shoreline which is as much as 16 km (10 miles) in length. More than one breeding female may exist within each male territory, and when the dog otter has a couple of bitches then each female will have her own range. The amount of seaboard which an otter controls depends upon its status within the local community of otters, and border conflicts erupt until the scale of dominance has been established.

Otters are well equipped for life in cold, murky waters. Their dense fur prevents the water from reaching and chilling their skin and when swimming their strong tails act as rudders. Meanwhile, the animals can use the whiskers around their muzzles to sense for prey in the darkest of underwater settings, and their ears and nostrils can be closed to exclude any water. Otters are extremely hardy and can breed at any season of the year, although most cubs appear in the early spring and are born in a nursery chamber of a 'holt' excavated in a waterside bank. Normally three in number, the cubs are reared together through their first year. In Scotland the coastal otter populations seem to have been maintained in

A common seal emerging for air

recent years despite the increasing threat from oil spillages. The inland populations have fared less well, partly because of the loss of riverside cover, partly because of growing levels of disturbance by fishing and boating and partly through the pollution of rivers by pesticides.

In 1990 the ravages of a seal distemper epidemic highlighted the plight of the European seal populations. Two types of seal inhabit the coasts of Britain: the common seal and the grey seal. Both have short, dense coats of blotched and spotted greyish fur and both display colour variations ranging from silver-grey to almost black. The grey seal is slightly larger and bulls can be 2.5 m (7 or 8 feet) long, while common seal bulls are around 30 cm (1 foot) shorter. However, the most obvious difference concerns the shape of the head: that of the grey seal being rather dog-like and that of the

Left: Evicted from most British rivers, the otter still thrives along many northern shores

common seal resembling a plump and appealing puppy. The two seals also differ in their chosen settings and in their breeding habits. The grey seal has established colonies on the Farne islands but it is essentially a creature of the rocky western shores and flourishes on deserted, storm-lashed coasts from Cornwall to the Outer Hebrides and the Northern Isles. These animals do not become fully mature until their fifth or sixth year. Late in the summer breeding season seals gather in colonies which are mainly on small, inaccessible islands. Each bull fiercely defends his territory and seeks to control as many females as possible, foregoing any attempt to feed until the mating season is over. Almost a year passes before the young are born, the mothers seeking out caves and sheltered crannies along the wild and windy coast. At first the baby seal is helpless, obvious in its snow-white coat and completely dependent upon its mother for food and protection. Unable even to swim, for the first fortnight of its life it remains hidden in a cave or stranded on a desolate islet. Meanwhile, the harassed mother starves until her calf is weaned. Then she resumes feeding, mates, moults and regains her strength during a period of intensive feeding.

Although herds of several dozen grey seals will sometimes gather, the common seal is a more sociable animal. While it may be found in Atlantic waters, it is largely a seal of North Sea shores and it prefers sand banks and mud-flats to rocky coasts. Herds of a hundred or more may be seen on the mud-flats around the Wash. Common seals do not display the highly territorial breeding habits of their grey cousins; they mate in the water in the weeks following the birth of the young. The seals are born in mid-summer and are much more independent, often taking to the water with their mothers on the tide which follows their birth.

Further north in the Atlantic the seal populations are culled by the killer whale, but in British waters man was these animals' only serious enemy. There is no doubt that they consume large quantities of fish, but neither can there be any real doubt that the severe depletion of fish stocks is a consequence of over-fishing by man, with the quantities taken by seals being quite incidental. The depletion of fish stocks may explain why seals have recently broken into commercial fish farms in search of food. Seals have suffered prolonged persecution and even today fishermen seem far more ready to decry the seals' assaults upon the fish stocks than their own. The grey seal takes commercial fish species but a considerable proportion of its diet is composed of the less palatable and uneconomic fish of the rocky shore. Shellfish, crabs, lobsters, wrasse, lumpsucker, conger eel, pollack, whiting, skate, ray, herring and salmon are all taken. The common seal is also an opportunistic feeder and is particularly partial to flounders.

Long ago, when the climate was glacial, walrus swam in British waters. A few walrus were recorded here early in the nineteenth century, and these must have been individuals swept southwards from sub-Arctic latitudes. Three other types of seal are very occasionally reported, the ringed seal, the harp seal and the hooded seal. In each case the animals concerned must have found themselves stranded upon decaying ice floes which eventually disintegrated within swimming distance of the British coast.

Chapter Five

The Wildlife of Dunes,
Salt-marshes and
Estuaries

The coastal setting contains several quite different habitats, each one narrow and confined by neighbouring habitats which are also quite distinct in their demands, constraints and opportunities. The plants and animals which flourish in the contrasting environments of dunes, estuaries and salt-marshes generally include some which are specially adapted to accept the challenges posed by the setting and others which are found elsewhere, but which are flexible and so able to tap the resources of a less familiar world. For example, the birdlife of the salt-marshes includes a few land birds, such as meadow pipits, lapwings and sky larks, birds of the estuarine mud-flats and shore, such as redshanks and shelduck, as well as birds which commonly nest on shingle beaches, notably the common tern. But there are other coastal species which are narrowly specialised to occupy a particular niche and are ill-equipped for life anywhere else, such as the salt-tolerant sea lavender which carpets the middle levels of many salt-marshes.

The salt-marsh does not exist as a stable environment but as a meeting place between two worlds: a place which is undergoing a slow transition from shore to land. At one time salt-marsh habitats were extensive around the British coasts, but since Roman times, if not before, the reclamation of existing salt-marshes has greatly exceeded the natural formation of new ones. It may be because of the impermanence of the salt-marsh setting that, while it has its own distinctive and specialised plants, its animal community is composed of visitors and immigrants from the margins: land creatures which are able to tolerate the salty conditions and animals of the wet, muddy shore which are able to cope with the greater dryness of the adjacent marshes.

Salt-marshes may form where the gradients between land and sea are very shallow. In such places the tide-swept zone is a broad one and the gentle slopes allow silts to be deposited by the waters of the sea and creeks, rather than being swept away. These silts are exceedingly fertile as both the tides and any incoming rivers are rich in detritus. They abound in nutrients and support vast

Previous page:
*Large numbers of lapwing
may migrate to coastal
mud-flats during cold
spells*

numbers of small shellfish, yet any plants or creatures seeking to exploit this richness are confronted with the problems of salinity. Eel-grass is a plant of muddy shores and estuaries which is capable of growing both in the inter-tidal zone and down below the low watermark. Although it resembles a seaweed it is, in fact, a flowering plant, its small, green flowers being remarkable in that they are pollinated under the water. Eel-grass provides valuable grazing for the flocks of brent geese but it is more important for the way in which it shields, binds and stabilises the muds. The other plants of the salt-marsh are all land plants which have evolved in ways which allow them to claim niches within the marsh, where the zoning of the plants reflects the successive stages in its colonisation.

At the lowest level of the marsh are those plants which are equipped to survive immersion by the salty tidal waters for several hours of each day. Here one may find glassworts and rice grass, with the rice grass maintaining a foothold in places where the currents are too strong for the shallow-rooted glassworts. Like the seablite, which may be found growing nearby, glasswort is an annual plant with a succulent, segmented stem and tiny green flowers. All these plants help to trap mud and plant debris amongst their stems and to reduce the force of the tidal currents, and so they serve as pioneers which prepare the land for colonisation by slightly more fastidious species. One of the most remarkable of the salt-marsh pioneers is the common cord grass, a natural hybrid between a native and a North American cord grass. This spiky grass appears to have made its debut in Southampton Water during the nineteenth century, and has subsequently spread widely, competing with and smothering native salt-marsh species, and even extending its range into the territory of the eel-grass.

Another grass, the sea manna grass, forms a turf above the glasswort and intermingles with the seablite, its tufted carpet providing a most effective trap for the silts washed in on the tides. Sea purslane, a spreading, shrubby plant with grey-green leaves and tiny greenish flowers, is one more plant which helps to build up the marsh by trapping silt. It lines the banks of the tidal creeks where the soil is less saturated, although it will tolerate a regular submergence by the tides.

If the plants of the lower marsh are more notable for their adaptations for survival in a setting which is salty and frequently submerged, those of the middle levels include some colourful members whose flowers create a summer carnival of lilac and

pink. The sea aster has flowers like those of a Michaelmas daisy, and has demonstrated a remarkable opportunism in recent years: its ability to tolerate a saline environment has allowed the plant to colonise the verges of motorways which are contaminated by the spreading of salt in winter. But the most striking plant of the middle marsh is the sea lavender; although its flowers are of a lavender hue, their form reveals its kinship to the popular garden everlasting, statice. Sea lavender can form an almost continuous carpet, but as the ground becomes drier it surrenders the stage to thrift, which can form a turf above which its pink-like flower heads shiver and shimmer in the breeze. As one moves to the higher levels of the marsh, so the importance of an ability to tolerate salt and submergence decreases. The plants growing in these levels may only experience submergence occasionally, during the highest of tides. Grasses such as the red fescue become common and reeds and rushes are able to survive in the less saline soils. Here the more natural coastal landscape yields to an artificial one created by land-hungry farmers.

The salt-marshes are created by the sea in its constructive guise, working with the assistance of plants which sieve out the silts carried by the tides. Were the activities entirely constructive then salt-marshes would be a most impermanent feature and would rapidly become dry land. However, the regular scouring of the winding marsh creeks by the advancing and retreating tides tends to preserve the habitats and to keep the marshes open to the sea. Any natural sea-to-land transition has been greatly outstripped by man's reclamation schemes. Around the Wash there are traces of successive sea walls which are the landmarks of a campaign to wrest new land from the sea which goes back more than a thousand years. The succulent salt-marsh plants and grasses always offered superb grazing and the walls were built to exclude the sea from these rich pastures. Several years after reclamation, the sea salt was flushed from the soil by rainfall, allowing arable crops to be grown, though in areas such as Kent's Romney Marsh the land was reserved for sheep, a local breed being developed which flourishes particularly well on the reclaimed grazings.

One of the most important of the differences between the salt-marsh and the estuarine habitats concerns the salinity levels, the waters of the estuaries being too fresh for conventional marine life and yet too salty for most freshwater creatures. Yet in the realm of birdlife there is an overlap across the estuarine, salt-marsh and mud-flat environments, with several species of wader, duck and goose being attracted to the rich food stores which they support. The permanent inhabitants of estuarine waters and tidal mud-flats must be able to tolerate conditions which are never stable. The state of the tide, the force and level of the incoming river and the strength of the waves all affect the levels of freshness and salinity at any particular place. Nor is there always a steady gradient of increasing brackishness as one moves from the land to the sea. Instead, and unless the waters have been thoroughly churned up by the waves and tide, the river water will tend to rise above the denser seawater, so that water which may be quite fresh at the surface can become fairly salty by the time the bed of the estuary is reached. In fact, a complex array of physical laws affects the estuarine environment. At high tide the temporary rise of the sea level creates a barrage against the inrush of a river, which can cause the level of the river to rise far upstream. The most notable case is the tidal bore on the Severn, which is experienced far up the river past Worcester during the spring tides.

As with the salt-marshes, the flora and fauna are composed of a mixture of native specialists and hardy intruders. Green seaweeds are able to colonise the fresher waters where the brown seaweeds cannot survive, while specialised species of sandhopper, ragworm, snail and acorn-barnacle have evolved which are able to regulate and maintain the salinity levels in their bodies and so to flourish in brackish waters. Intruders include sea- or river-water creatures which have proved able to accept a wide spectrum of conditions. They comprise flounders and some shore animals, including the periwinkle and shore crab. There are also opportunists, such as some species of shrimp, which will drift in and out of the brackish waters depending on the prevailing levels of salinity. Finally, there are the supremely adaptable fish which pass through the estuaries in transit between saltwater and freshwater habitats. Salmon and sea-trout swim upstream to the headwaters of the less polluted rivers to spawn, while eels enter rivers as youngsters, remain in them until they are mature, and then head for their spawning grounds in the distant ocean. The flounder almost qualifies for this category; its eggs hatch offshore and then the young fish move through the estuary into relatively fresh waters, where they remain for two or three years before returning to the sea to spawn.

Because of the layering of fresh and salt waters, found in some estuaries, like that of the Tees, but less apparent in others, like that of the Severn, one can find situations in which fish from upstream, such as the roach, three-spined stickleback and bream, are living in the upper, fresher levels, while the saltier waters just below them are supporting grey mullet, goby and flounder. But in order to make a complete transition from marine to river life fish such as salmon, sea-trout, sturgeon and the less well known shad and smelt, all of which enter rivers to spawn, must be able to control the balance of salt in their bodies. They have a level of blood salt which is between that of sea and river water, and to maintain it they must drink great quantities of water and release surplus salts through special cells in their gills when at sea and excrete large amounts of water when in rivers.

The constant influx of silt- and nutrient-rich river water and the washing and churning action of the tides produces a wealth of food, ranging from plankton to tightly packed masses of mussels. And so it is not surprising that the estuarine habitat is exceedingly attractive to birdlife. The diversity of the bird species which can be seen is also remarkable; several seem superficially similar, but each is precisely tailored to secure a little niche in the great coastal restaurant. As we have seen, the lengths of legs and bills equip the different species to exploit a particular vein of prey without trespassing on the food resources upon which other species rely. While some of the estuarine birds, such as the grey plover, favour fairly solitary existences, others, such as knots, find advantages in flocking as more eyes are available to perceive predators and birds of prey may become confused amongst the wheeling mass. A feeding flock is unlikely to take to the air when but one of its

The otherwise conspicuous plumage of the ringed plover provides good camouflage when it is nesting on shingle beaches

members takes flight, but a mass lift-off seems to be triggered when a critical number of individuals are startled into flight.

When one sees flocks of knots and bar-tailed godwits interspersed with oystercatchers, dunlin, sandpipers and ringed plover the impression may be one of chaotic feeding, but actually competition is reduced by habits as well as physiology. The pat-

The distinctive oyster-catcher has a sturdy bill designed for heavy work

terns of feeding are regulated by the tides, which expose different sections of mud-flat and salting at different times. The various species also feed for different periods; the curlew, for example, does its wading and probing for only half the tidal cycle, while the hungry dunlin is at work for three-quarters of it. The waders do not rely on sight alone to locate their prey, and so birds such as the oystercatcher can continue to feed during the long nights of winter, when it uses its sturdy bill to skim through the silt until a cockle is located. The abrasive action of the mud and sand particles would soon wear down the bills of the wading birds were their tips not in a constant state of renewal. As the year goes by so the food resources change; most of the young shellfish and other invertebrate prey may have been consumed, but those that have evaded the waders have grown, so that the morsels on offer are far fewer but much larger.

Unlike most land birds, which build elaborate and well-camouflaged nests and devote enormous energies to feeding their

107

fledglings, the waders tend to be thrust into the hardships of the world directly after hatching. Oystercatchers are an exception, for while their nest is a mere scrape in the sand or shingle, the parents do bring food to their offspring and teach them how to spear open shells. The young that survive inherit a voracious appetite, eating their own weight in mussels and mud worms every day. Although equipped with wading legs of a moderate length, these birds, unmistakable in their black and white plumage, tend to take their food from the mud-flats newly exposed by the tide, following the sea in and out but showing a greater respect for any stronger-than-expected waves than do the plucky godwits. Dunlin, mottled brown above with speckled throats, black breasts and white underparts, are the commonest of the waders. They are often seen in flocks, probing the muds with bills of a medium length which are capable of reaching a little deeper than those of the little ringed plovers which peck and scurry across the bare sands.

In winter there are changes to the cast of players. There is a southerly drift of oystercatchers, some British breeders moving to the shores of Spain to be replaced by birds from Scandinavia. Lapwing and golden plover arrive in the saltings from their breeding places in the uplands and other golden plover arrive from Iceland and the continent. Curlews also make the move from the moorlands and high pastures to the coast and great flocks of little grey knot may be seen around the estuaries of northern England, arriving in July and departing in March for their breeding grounds in Greenland and Siberia. Sanderling, grey plover, black and bar-tailed godwits and turnstone are other winter visitors to the nutrient-rich waters of our estuaries.

Ducks and geese may be seen feeding close to the waders but they are built according to quite different principles of bird design, with the emphasis on floating rather than wading. The shelduck, resplendent with its bottle-green head, white body and brick-red breast band, is widespread around British estuaries and is specially adapted to sift small hydrobia snails from the estuarine ooze. Its bill has comb-like margins and as the bird follows the ebb tide it swings its head back and forth over the muds so that the snails are trapped and the mud is filtered away. Shelduck favour shallow shores without cliffs and are widely distributed, with some favoured estuaries and bays supporting more than a thousand pairs. The birds nest amongst dunes, marshes and in coastal plantations, but in summer, when the young birds have fledged,

Like geese, wigeon graze on grass and they nest beside northern coastal waters

the shelduck migrate to assemble in great numbers in moulting areas. The main one is the Heligoland Bight, a sea area off the Elbe estuary, although several thousand birds favour Bridgwater Bay in Somerset. When moulting is over they return to their old haunts around our shores.

Much rarer and even more colourful is the little wigeon, the male being magnificent with his grey and white barred flanks, claret head and breast, and yellow head flash. Unlike the shelduck, the wigeon is a vegetarian and content to feed on grass. Although a rare breeder in the north of Scotland and a few locations in the uplands of northern England, vast flocks of wigeon arrive as winter visitors to some British coastal waters, the total of birds arriving from northern Russia and Scandinavia being around 200,000. Of these visitors, some 35,000 come inland to the Ouse Washes in East Anglia, while another 10,000 settle around the Wash, and great flocks congregate in the Dornoch Firth, Cromarty Firth, Montrose Basin and southern estuaries such as the Medway.

Several other species of duck are less frequently glimpsed around the British coast. Pintail are rare as breeders but around 25,000 of these striking duck winter in Britain, favouring marshes, flooded ground and estuaries. Scaup are even rarer as breeders, but as winter visitors they are almost as numerous as the pintail.

Pintail duck have bred in Britain since 1869 and may be seen on both inland and coastal waters

They form small groups dotted around the coast but in certain favoured estuaries and inlets, such as the Firth of Forth, Dornoch Firth and Humber, they congregate in large flocks. The eider is very much a sea duck and breeds in many remote locations around the Scottish coast and in some places along the east coast of England. It is a large duck and is equipped with a sturdy bill, allowing it to feed on well-armoured creatures such as mussels, cockles, razor-shells, crabs and sea urchins. Eider are sociable birds, forming breeding colonies on small islands and on both rocky shores and sand dune systems. In Iceland the nests of this white, black, pink and green duck are still raided to obtain soft down from the brownish female, which is used to stuff eider-downs. Although there is a small-scale migration of continental eider duck into southern England, most of the birds encountered in winter have drifted southwards from their Scottish strong-holds. The largest flocks gather in the Firth of Forth and around the mouths of the Tay and Ythan, but eider may also be seen in winter in many places around the shores of England. Other ducks which may occasionally be seen around our coasts include the goldeneye, long-tailed, and the common, surf and velvet scoters.

Several species of goose visit Britain, and although it may be easy to distinguish at a distance between the grey and the black-necked types, the recognition of particular species is not always easy. The pink-footed is the smallest and the most numerous of the grey geese. In October the entire Greenland and Icelandic population, amounting to around 75,000 birds, arrives in Britain.

Scaup feed on molluscs and move to coastal waters in winter, where they eat mussels

Often flocks settle in certain favoured arrival places, including the estuaries of the Tay and Humber and the Wash, although many birds winter around inland waters. Pink-footed geese can be seen grazing saltings, but they will also move to pastures or cause damage to young cereal crops. The white-fronted goose is rather similar in appearance, but it has a white patch around the base of its bill. There are two sub-species; the European bird winters in Holland, with around 6,000 of these geese continuing westward to southern England and Wales, while around 4,500 white-fronts from Greenland move to the shores and lochs of western Scotland and north Wales. As with the pink-foots, these geese have moved

An eider duck just completing its moult

The pink-footed goose may be seen in winter on the coasts of eastern Scotland and northern England

The lesser white-fronted goose is a sporadic winter visitor to British waters, when other white-fronts arrive from Greenland and northern Russia

on to farmland as the grazings of the salt-marshes have been reclaimed. The small native population of greylag geese includes both wild birds which breed in the far north-west of Scotland and domesticated birds which have returned to the wild, but in the autumn these birds are vastly outnumbered by around 60,000 greylags arriving from Iceland and colonising lochs and estuaries as far south as Morecambe Bay.

The black-necked geese include brent geese and barnacle geese, the latter easily recognised by its large white face patch. Here again there are two distinct populations; the one which breeds in Spitzbergen, an island north of Norway, numbering around 3,000 and wintering on the Solway Firth, while 25,000 barnacle geese from Greenland winter in the Hebrides, mainly on Islay. The brent goose is another winter visitor and it occurs in two easily recognised strains. The dark-bellied form breeds in Siberia, and in late autumn around 40,000 of these birds colonise the southern coasts from the Wash to Devon. Meanwhile, around 1,000 light-bellied brent geese, which breed in Greenland and Canada, spill over from the main wintering grounds in Denmark and settle around the coasts of north-east England. Brent geese favour eel-grass, but will also graze on saltings and on arable crops. The geese which winter in Britain breed and dwell in the summer on the sub-arctic tundra, and have learned to colonise farmland as

The greylag goose once bred as far south as the Fens, but became rare away from the moors and sea lochs of Scotland

the salt-marsh vegetation which provided their main winter feeding grounds has been reclaimed. Pressure from hunting and persecution by farmers have taken a toll of their numbers; the depredations of brent geese in East Anglia is still a controversial issue, while in the past barnacle geese suffered heavily from over-shooting.

Swans are not normally regarded as coastal birds, but all three types can be seen in estuarine waters. The mute swan, our most familiar swan of lakes and canals, is the one least likely to be seen at sea. It is generally regarded as the heaviest flying bird in the world and can sometimes be seen offshore at places such as

Chichester and Lindisfarne. The whooper swan is almost as large and has its breeding grounds in the north of Iceland. The great majority of these Icelandic birds winter in Britain, where they become scattered amongst inland and coastal sites. The greatest assemblages are found on Scottish lochs but other groups can be seen on the Solway Firth, Ythan estuary, Beauly Firth and around Lindisfarne. Bewick's swan has a black and yellow bill rather like that of the whooper but is of a lighter build. It breeds in the north of Siberia and winters in western Europe. Once these swans favoured wintering grounds in Scotland, but during the past sixty years they have preferred inland locations in southern England. Around 1,000 Bewick's, amounting to about half the British wintering population, visit the Ouse Washes, where they are well fed and protected. The patterning of black and yellow on the bill of this swan varies from individual to individual, and this has enabled researchers to recognise particular birds and to study their habits and lifespan.

It would be hard to imagine two habitats as different as those of the flat, wet estuarine muds and the parched, hummocky and shifting world of the sand dunes. In fact, these habitats frequently exist side by side, as around the Ythan estuary, while birdlife may overlap the two settings. Although the dunes support only a rather sparse and restricted range of flora, their growth is in some ways dependent upon plant life. The dunes begin to grow when sands blown in from the beach accumulate around an obstruction, such as a boulder or stump. But such sand mounds can grow no taller than the obstruction around which the sands rest, and to heighten and broaden, the mound must be colonised by plants which will trap the drifting sands around their stems and roots. Sea couch grass and the pink-flowered sea rocket may begin the process, but marram grass is by far the most important of the colonists, and as the dune rises so the grass rises with it. Its network of roots burrows deeply into the unstable sands, binding the dune together, while lateral branches fork outwards in all directions until the dune may be enmeshed by a single plant. At this stage, the surface of the dune will still have a tufty appearance and the areas of bare sand between the marram clumps are exposed to the winds and become liable to experience blow-outs. Gap-fillers which colonise these spaces include the sea spurge, sea holly and sea bindweed, the latter having pink, trumpet-shaped flowers like those of the more familiar bindweed, but a prostrate habit and creeping stems which twine amongst the loose sand.

The dune is still unstable. Gusting gales, burrowing by rabbits or excessive trampling may still punch gaps through the cover, which will open the way for more severe blow-outs. With much sand still exposed, such dunes are known as 'yellow dunes'. They become stable 'grey dunes' as the marram is replaced by other creeping grasses, the sand sedge and the red fescue, while mosses and grey lichens blanket any gaps and give the dune its change of hue. Within two or three centuries an area of unstable dunes could become a lowland heath carpeted in heather, and liable to yield in turn to birch woodland. Alternatively, such an area could be colonised for farming or else become a coniferous plantation or a golf links.

The valleys between the dunes are known as 'slacks' and here the low-lying ground is damper and may even have standing water. The less arduous conditions allow a wider range of flora and fauna to be supported, so that worms appear and insect life becomes more diverse. A lovely wild orchid, the marsh hellebor-ine, may move in from nearby marshes and the creeping willow gains its footholds. This is really a heathland shrub, and the only true seashore shrub, with a high tolerance of sandy soils and salty winds, is the sea buckthorn. Heavily armoured with thorns and with masses of white blossom which is followed by heavy crops of

The bright blue flowers of the viper's bugloss may be found among dunes and on sea cliffs. The plant was regarded as a cure for snake-bite

bitter, orange berries, the sea buckthorn is sometimes planted on dunes to speed up the stabilisation process. Another distinctive shrub of the dune belt is the delightful burnet rose, which is also at home on the limestone uplands. It has upright stems covered in narrow thorns and large, white, yellow-centred flowers. One of the most striking plants of the dune slacks is the viper's bugloss, with stalks bristling with blue flowers. Other notable plants are the storksbill, a wild geranium with purple or whitish flowers which may last for but a morning, and the biting stonecrop, which has fleshy leaves and tufty yellow flowers.

Unlike the estuarine muds, the parched sands of the dunes do not provide important feeding grounds for birds. Flies, which lay their eggs in carrion stranded on the beach, are numerous and so too are snails, particularly if the dune sands are rich in the lime needed for shell-building. Shelduck make their burrows in the sands, using the dunes as a home base for feeding forays to nearby estuaries, and colonies of gulls may also be supported.

Nesting amongst undisturbed sand dunes, on low islets, off-shore sand bars, shingle beaches, rocky islands and even by inland waters, terns are not easily ascribed to any particular habitat. These agile and graceful birds are sometimes known as 'sea swallows', and with their snow-white plumage and forked tails they do seem to combine the grace of the swallow and the sea-gull. They have stiletto-like bills, reminiscent of some waders, and webbed feet like the ducks, although these features do not provide a clear clue to their feeding habits. Terns do not wade and only seldom choose to swim. Instead, they catch their food by hovering over the water on flickering, pointed wings, their heads down and eyes scouring the waves, until a small fish is spotted and the bird plunges to seize it in its bill. Terns are most numerous in the Pacific, but are distributed throughout the world in no less than thirty-nine main species and several sub-species. They are sociable birds which nest in large colonies; one in the Seychelles, composed of sooty terns, contains more than a million pairs.

Several types of tern nest around the British coast and there can be no doubt that the most remarkable of these is the Arctic tern. It is thought that some members of this species enjoy more hours of daylight than any other animal, for they spend their summers enjoying the midnight sun of Arctic latitudes and 'winter' in the perpetual daylight of the Antarctic. Migration tracks vary, but flights are known to take birds from Britain, Greenland and Newfoundland to southern Africa. In the course of a year, some individuals will have flown more than 32,000 km (20,000 miles) in their migration flights. It appears that the Arctic terns do not begin to nest until they are at least three years old and may live to be twenty years of age. Britain lies at the southern margin of the breeding range of the Arctic tern. The largest colonies are on Westray and Papa Westray in the Orkneys, with almost 30,000 pairs; a third as many nest in the Shetlands, and the Farnes, with 3,000 pairs, support the largest English colonies, although much smaller communities can be found dotted around the coast as far south as Chesil Beach.

Other terns nesting in Britain include the common tern, only distinguishable from its Arctic cousin by experienced bird-watchers. However, its main colonies lie to the south of a line drawn from the Mersey to the Tyne, and any tern seen on most English coasts is more likely to be of the common variety. The lovely roseate tern, with its breast flushed in pink, is one of our rarer breeding seabirds and only around 1,500 pairs breed here, in widely scattered colonies. The sandwich tern frequents the Atlantic margins and the Black and Caspian Seas. Its heartland was in Holland but since the 1950s pesticide residues have reduced the Dutch population of this tern from around 35,000 to just a few hundred. In Britain the number of sandwich terns has been more stable, though somewhat declining, and, while form-ing new colonies, these terns will suddenly desert established ones. The sandwich tern is the largest of the British terns, with the exception of the magnificent Caspian tern, which is occasionally seen as a stray from the Scandinavian breeding flock. The diminu-tive little tern is also an erratic breeder which requires special protection. It nests very close to the high watermark at shoreline sites which are prone to disturbance by human visitors. The black tern is a very rare but unmistakable breeding bird and the gull-billed tern has bred here on just one or two occasions; the whis-kered tern and white-winged black tern are occasionally glimpsed as migrants.

Chapter Six

THE ARMOURED COAST

Not only has the course of British history been guided by the island character of the homeland, but so too have our outlooks. The great nations of the continent have seen their territories expand, contract or fall according to the shifts in the patterns of power. The existence of land frontiers made the threats of surprise attack and invasion much more immediate, though at the same time the permeability of these frontiers encouraged contact between neighbouring peoples. Hemmed around by the sea, the peoples of England, Scotland and Wales were compelled to reach some form of accommodation within Britain – but they were also endowed with the ability to stand aloof from continental affairs, intervening or withdrawing almost at will, while establishing trans-Atlantic and imperial contacts which could not instantly be threatened by the machinations of a hostile neighbour. Today, the insular mentality of the British may frustrate our partners and undermine our own best interests, but in the past the sense of security which the sea-girt setting fostered encouraged adventurous and independent outlooks and nurtured the growth of nationhood. Even so, the threat of invasion was never completely extinguished and the inheritance from the history-long preoccupation with invasion scares – so many of them more imagined than real – is a vulgar xenophobia which the gutter press still seems able to ignite at will. From the days of the earliest kingdoms the rulers of Britain have appreciated the simple fact that their independence would survive so long as the approaches could be swept free of foreign fleets and the shores armoured in such ways that no invasion force could establish a beachhead.

The earliest British people were not islanders. Rather, they were hunters and fisherfolk who had drifted northwards across the low marshes and mud-flats at the base of what was then a thumb-like appendage of the European continent. Some groups moved along the coast from strand to strand, leaving behind great middens of shells from the molluscs which they had eaten – huge mounds which can still be recognised on some Scottish shores. Other groups wandered down to the coast in winter, when inland food sources were in short supply.

Around ten thousand years ago, the rising sea was lapping across the fringes of the plains and marshes, until eventually the

The Rumps, a Cornish cliff castle

land link to the continent was severed. For many centuries most communities in Britain would have been oblivious or indifferent to the fact that they were islanders, and throughout the whole of prehistoric time there was no sense of a national identity. Neighbours living in adjacent tribal territories must, for most of the time, have been far more feared than any alien, sea-borne forces. However, it is unlikely that trading contacts with the continent were ever allowed to stagnate, and many of the artefacts recovered by excavators at sites belonging to all the prehistoric periods arrived as trade goods brought from abroad. Metal ores were traded with Mediterranean societies and it is probable that fishermen plied between the Channel coasts.

Organised commerce with its own trading ports existed from at least the Bronze Age, although much remains to be discovered. One Bronze Age trading port was at Hengistbury Head in Dorset. Early in the Iron Age, which began around 650 BC, a number of trade links existed. Goods from the continent were shipped up the Thames, while others entered England via the Humber. The West Country was engaged in an active trade with Iberia and the Mediterranean, one of the ports which operated then being sited at Mount Batten, by Plymouth Sound. Metals, mainly tin but also lead, copper and iron, were the main British exports, while bronze goods, trinkets and wine were imported.

Around 150 BC, the commerce of the old port at Hengistbury Head greatly revived. Ships from the continent anchored in the natural harbour, which was sheltered by a headland fortified by two lines of ramparts. Glassware from the Mediterranean, pottery from Brittany, coins from northern France and amphorae of Italian wine all entered this bustling port. Poole Harbour had also emerged as a busy commercial focus, and the land trade routes leading to and from these Dorset ports were overlooked and guarded by the gigantic hillfort, Maiden Castle. Trade also involved British communities well away from the Channel shores; Scottish societies had some form of contact with lands across the North Sea basin, while a lead anchor stock from a Mediterranean Iron Age ship has been discovered in the treacherous waters off the Lleyn Peninsula in North Wales. In the decades before the Roman invasion, the commercial heartland of England shifted to the south-east and new trading posts, such as Colchester, emerged. Other ports were established further afield, including Ferriby on the Humber estuary; there was probably a port at Selsey Bill in Sussex, while the veteran port of Hengistbury continued to prosper. The further that one looks back in time the harder it becomes to gain a clear picture of coastal life. On the Lincolnshire coast between Mablethorpe and Skegness traces of New Stone Age and Bronze Age settlements have been discovered, and it appears that a salt-making industry existed here during many prehistoric centuries.

In 1136, Tintagel in Cornwall was said by the Welsh cleric, Geoffrey of Monmouth, to have been the place where King Arthur was conceived in the course of a passionate encounter between King Uther Pendragon and Igraine, the wife of a rival ruler. Although no experts credited this account, it did give rise to a local Arthurian tourist industry. The real castle on the cliffs at Tintagel is much less controversial; it was begun within a few years of Geoffrey's writing about Tintagel by the Earl of Cornwall. Few castles had a more rugged and salty setting, for the sea separated the rest of the castle from its outer bailey. However, the sea proved to be an aggressor as well as a defender, and in 1538 the antiquary, John Leland, described what remained of Tintagel castle: 'The residue of the buildings of this castle be sore weather beaten . . . belike it had three wards but two be worn away by the gulping in of the sea insomuch that it has made almost an isle.' There is no doubt that the castle postdates the era of the mythical King Arthur by several centuries but in 1983 a grass fire scorched the ground and revealed the traces of dozens of huts which could date from the Dark Ages. Tintagel has long been regarded as the setting of an ancient monastery of the Celtic church, but now some are seeing it as having been a more influential and substantial place during the fifth and sixth centuries: perhaps the capital of a local ruler. At the time of writing excavations are in progress here, and if successful they may place Tintagel in a tradition which goes back into prehistoric time. For the moment it is ironic that while visitors flock to see a place of uncertain pedigree almost all of them are unaware that the coasts on either side are studded with strongholds of an undisputed prehistoric provenance.

So often when walking the cliff tops one will see the overgrown traces of banks and ditches running across the neck of a promontory. Probably not one rambler in a hundred will pause to wonder about the significance of the earthworks or ponder on their age. During the last fifteen centuries or so of the pre-Christian era local fortifications were extremely important in Britain. Inland communities frequently created their strongholds by ringing a whole summit or ridge in a girdle of ramparts and ditches, but for those living near to a rocky coast the business of defence could be made a great deal easier. Instead of expending the immense toil involved in creating a hillfort, the people could hew and pile a ditch and rampart across the neck of a cliff-girt headland – and so create a fortified bolt-hole which was every bit as secure as some of the strongest inland hillforts. Known to archaeologists as 'promontory forts' or 'cliff castles', most of these strongholds date from the Iron Age, although some were redeveloped during the turmoil of the Dark Ages.

They were emphatically not coastal defences intended to protect the shores of a kingdom against alien seaborne invaders. Rather, they provided individual communities and their petty rulers with refuges which could be defended against attack by their neighbours on the land. Some cliff castles contain traces of dwellings to show that a part of the population lived permanently inside the stronghold, and like the hillforts of the interior, these forts will sometimes have served as local capitals and trading centres.

Defensible rocky promontories are most numerous on the western shores of Britain and so too, not surprisingly, are the cliff castles. Within England and Wales they are heavily concentrated in Cornwall and in the old county of Pembrokeshire; most of the remainder lie in Devon and the old counties of Caernarvonshire, Glamorgan and Anglesey. One of the most striking examples is Rame Head in Cornwall, where less than 100 m (about 100 yards) of bank and ditch were sufficient to sever a virtual island of land around 400 m (¼ mile) in diameter. The Rumps is a better-known Cornish example; originally the promontory seems to have been used as a stock pen, with a stone wall running across its neck to serve as a cattle fence. It was converted into a cliff castle when double ramparts and ditches were added. The outlines of contemporary circular huts have been recognised inside the defences. Gurnard's Head is another well-known Cornish example, while the most elaborate fortifications in the county are found at Trevelgue, with no less than seven sets of banks and ditches. It is thought that the cliff castle builders of Cornwall were immigrants from Brittany who settled here during the Iron Age, converting existing headland cattle enclosures into defensive refuges and living as herdsmen and traders.

Wooltack Point and Linney Head are two of the best Dyfed (Pembrokeshire) examples. At Linney Head the defended area covers just 0.3 ha (1 acre); sea cliffs stand guard on three sides and a complex pattern of earthworks defends the landward ap-

proaches. At Wooltack Point, however, just one line of ramparts was thought sufficient to fortify a much larger area, for a great natural gulley was there to serve as a ditch and the ramparts were built to overlook its western edge.

During the Dark Ages, when unstable chieftains and tyrants attempted to secure and expand their youthful kingdoms, some cliff castles gained a new lease of life. Castle Rock, Dumbarton, has been identified as 'the Rock of the Clyde' which was the Dark Age capital of the British kingdom of Strathclyde. The rock is a volcanic plug which is partly split by a natural cleft and which stands in the Clyde estuary on an isthmus flanked by the Clyde and the Leven. Before the Clyde was artificially deepened to allow ships access to Glasgow, the rock stood at the head of navigation. In 870–1, however, this rugged capital was stormed by the forces of two Irish Vikings, Olafr and Ivarr; shortly afterwards they returned with two hundred ships and took many English, British and Pictish slaves away with them to Dublin. On the coast of north-east Scotland, Dunottar, near Stonehaven, is a spectacular medieval castle standing on a promontory of reddish pudding stone. The history of defence here goes back beyond the Middle Ages, for this was almost certainly the fortress of Dun Fother, mentioned in the Annals of Iona in AD 681. Its fate was similar to that of Castle Rock, for other old annals reveal that Dun Fother was destroyed by 'gentiles' – meaning Vikings – in the reign of Donald, son of Constantine (AD 889–900). The rampart which was built to defend the Dark Age promontory fort is thought to have been incorporated into a much later defence against artillery bombardment. There must be several places where medieval or later coastal fortifications have obliterated the traces of Dark Age and prehistoric defenceworks – the sea stacks at Dunbar in the southeast of Scotland are almost certainly an example.

The cliff citadels and capitals of the Dark Ages owed more to the prehistoric tradition than to the Roman outlook on coastal defence. The Romans were the first rulers of England and Wales to take a coherent view of invasion threats and to form policies which sought to thwart piracy and raiding. Rome was a land power rather than a great sea power, and so the prospect of launching a seaborne invasion of the Celtic tribal kingdoms of Britain across a strange, wild and open sea must have unsettled commanders and troopers alike – but at least there was no British navy to worry about. The real practical problem was that of transporting a sophisticated army intact across more than 30 km (20 miles) of unfamiliar and potentially treacherous water. Romans were unequalled in their handling of practical problems, yet their campaign was almost undermined by psychological weaknesses. In the days of the invaders' great-grandfathers, some of the ships in Julius Caesar's raiding fleet had been wrecked in the course of an exploratory invasion of Britain, and in AD 40 a loss of resolve had led to the abandonment of an invasion planned by Caligula. But in the summer of AD 43 the conditions were more hopeful; Aulus Plautius had assembled a mighty fleet; the Roman commanders seemed to have the frightened and mutinous elements amongst their forces under control; and the merchants who traded across the Channel reported that the British forces were crumbling away as they saw harvest time approaching and supposedly the threat of an invasion receding.

The great fleet was divided into three components. Richborough in Kent was selected as the site for the main landing, but in order to divide and confuse any opposing forces a fleet was sent westwards to land its troops in the inlets somewhere near Chichester. Meanwhile, a third unit landed at a site which is now uncertain, probably either Deal or Reculver. The coastal geography at Richborough was then far different than today. A narrow channel, the Wantsum, separated the island of Thanet from the

The Roman lighthouse at Dover

mainland, and Richborough lay on the coast at the southern outlet of this channel (while Reculver lay at its northern end). It was endowed with a fine natural harbour which controlled both the approaches to the Channel and to the estuary of the Thames. The Roman landings were unopposed and, having failed to confront the invaders on the beaches, the British now faced the unenviable task of meeting elements of the greatest army in the world in a land battle. This took place at a ford on the Medway. In the course of a battle which lasted for two days, the forty thousand armoured and disciplined legionaries and auxiliaries proved more than a match for the brave but poorly marshalled tribesmen with their outmoded arms and uncoordinated tactics. As soon as the invaders had landed at Richborough they had begun to defend the bridgehead. A rampart fronted by two narrow ditches and almost a kilometre (half a mile) in length protected the Roman foothold. Forty years later a great triumphal arch festooned with statuary was erected here to commemorate the conquest, but before the Romans withdrew from Britain the function and appearance of Richborough would again be transformed, as we shall see.

With their bridgehead secure, the Roman armies were able to conquer the tribal territories piecemeal. Conquest was followed by pacification and, in the productive lowland areas, by civilisation. The Roman interest in coastal affairs was no greater than was necessary to supply, exploit and defend an island outpost of the empire. The Roman fleet in British waters, the 'Classis Britannia' had no great sea power to confront, and so its role became one of providing logistical support to the army. Its main bases were at Dover, at Lympne in Kent and across the Channel at Boulogne. After the suppression of the Boudicca uprising and about two decades after the initial conquest, London emerged as the great trading capital of the island, and merchant vessels must have bustled to and fro across the Channel and up and down the Thames estuary. Coastal traffic was also very active, with supplies for the occupying forces being moved by sea, river and canal. In the course of campaigning, coastal store bases were set up at places like South Shields, while most of the main fortresses had their own harbour installations, as at Caerleon, in the south of Wales, and Chester, and were accessible to shipping. The losses of ships along the wild and sometimes unfamiliar coasts must have been quite high, but we know of only two lighthouses which were built by the Romans. They stood at either side of the entrance to the harbour at Dover, and the one on the eastern side still stands as an impressive ruin. Hexagonal in shape, it would have originally stood about 24 m (80 feet) in height but now only the lower half of the Roman 'pharos' survives, crowned with 6 m (20 feet) of medieval masonry.

At first, the need for coastal defences seemed minimal. Anglesey had been a last bastion of illegal Druidism and insurgency, and in AD 60 Roman forces crossed the Menai Strait and stormed the island. In AD 78 a substantial auxiliary fort, Segontium, was built close to Caernarfon to guard the Menai Strait and control the agricultural wealth of Anglesey and the mining resources of Snowdonia. It was manned for three centuries.

Hadrian's Wall, built in the years following this emperor's visit to Britain in AD 122, and stretching across northern Britain from the Tyne to the Solway Firth, is the most familiar of the monuments to the Roman occupation of Britain. But it is not widely known that the system of fortifications and check-points continued down the Cumbrian coast from the end of the wall at Bowness. The milecastles and turrets which regularly punctuated the wall were duplicated along the coast by turf and timber milefortlets and stone towers. This system of coastal defences has been traced running southwards along the Cumbrian coast for almost 50 km (30 miles), but it is possible that it continued for a further 25 km (15 miles) to St Bees Head or even down to Ravenglass. Some important commanders plainly thought it necessary to fortify this storm-ridden section of coast in a far-flung backwater of the empire, although the reasons for doing so are not clear. Was the north of England exposed to seaborne raiders from the south of Scotland or from Ireland, or did the defenceworks simply represent the workings of rigid and bureaucratic minds operating far from the area concerned?

Later during the occupation, the need for coastal defences became indisputable, so that Britain gained its first coherent system of fortifications for national defence. Gone were the days when Roman sailors could be redeployed to work at the iron forges of the Weald, as had happened during the second century. To one side of the North Sea lay the rich, pacified and productive farmlands of Britain, studded with towns and stippled with well-appointed villas. Across the sea and beyond the control of the empire lay the plains, inlets and islands peopled by pagan Anglo-Saxon tribesmen, who had racy ships and a growing taste for piracy. At first there was little to prevent these raiders from emerging from the grey sea mists to anchor in a bay or sail upriver and plunder an unsuspecting community. By the middle of the third century the threat of Saxon raiding had grown to the point where national security itself was at risk, especially when the attention of the occupying forces was diverted by internal dissent and power struggles.

The victory monument at Richborough was rebuilt to serve more practical purposes, and became a fortified watch tower. During the last third of the century, vulnerable sections of the coast were defended by strong 'forts of the Saxon shore'. The coasts of Roman Gaul were also defended by a chain of forts, allowing the imperial fleet to work between the bases and intercept raiders arriving from the Saxon homelands.

Earlier forts existed at Brancaster in Norfolk and Reculver in Kent and new ones were built at Burgh Castle, Walton Castle and Bradwell in East Anglia and Essex and Portchester, Dover, Richborough and Lympne on the southern shores. The Lympne fort was superseded by one built at Pevensey in the 330s after it was wrecked by silting and landslips, and an additional fort may have existed at Carisbrooke Castle on the Isle of Wight. With the work complete, the new shore forts guarded the exposed invasion coast from the Wash to the Isle of Wight.

At Richborough, the ruins of the shore fort are still impressive. The enclosure, covering about 2.2 ha (5½ acres), was surrounded by massive walls of flint which stood within deep ditches. The spectacular four-way triumphal arch had been stripped of statuary and converted into a 27-m (90-foot) tall signal tower guarded by triple ditches, though all that survives today is its concrete base. When the shore fort was built these ditches were filled in, while nearby the visitor can see the foundations of shops and of an official staging post or inn, relics of more peaceful times before the site was fortified against the Saxon threat. Later, ruined shore forts like those at Burgh Castle and Reculver would seem to have had a special fascination for Christian missionaries, and at Richborough there are the outlines of an early Saxon church. Legends in this locality claim that St Augustine landed here in 597 on his way to convert the court of King Ethelbert. Impressive in a way that is more easily deciphered are the ruins at Burgh Castle, which was built on a river bluff overlooking the river Waveney. The large rectangular enclosure was defended by a thick wall built of alternating courses of flint nodules and narrow red bricks. Well after the start of the building works, the orders were changed and solid, drum-like bastions were added to the walls to provide platforms for 'ballistae' or artillery pieces.

The ruins of the fort at Pevensey in East Sussex are also still impressive. An oval piece of ground around 3.5 ha (9 acres) in area was enclosed by a circuit of walls which survives largely intact and still stands up to 7.5 m (25 feet) in height. Originally, the wall

was punctuated by fifteen U-shaped bastions, and entrance was gained via a massive gateway flanked by strong towers which contained guard chambers. Despite the strength of these fortifications, the Pevensey garrison was overrun and slaughtered in 491, when the fort was attacked by Aelle and his South Saxons. During the Norman era, the Roman walls were employed to form the bailey of the castle of Robert de Mortain, who built his keep in the south-east angle of the old defences.

Burgh Castle, the best-preserved of the Roman forts of the Saxon shore

No less imposing are the ruins of the shore fort of Portchester, at the head of Portsmouth harbour, where sections of wall stand more than 6 m (20 feet) tall and where fourteen from an original twenty hollow bastions still survive. Here again, the defensive qualities of the site were recognised in a later age, and in the 1120s Henry I built a castle in the north-west angle of the Roman walls.

With forts such as these the threat from the east was held at bay but never vanquished. In the meantime, a threat from the west began to materialise, for while a Roman invasion of Ireland may have been discussed it was never launched, and this free Celtic stronghold emerged as a base for piracy and raiding. Although the

*The ruins of Dun
Carloway broch on Lewis*

great fortress at Caerleon, near Newport, was abandoned early in the 4th century, new strongholds, similar to the forts guarding the Saxon shore, were built at Cardiff and Lancaster. Late in this century, the venerable fort at Caernarfon may have been super-seded by a new one overlooking the harbour at Holyhead. Across the country on the Yorkshire coast, a chain of signalling stations were in operation to provide early warning of raiders to the civilised populations of the interior and the garrison at York. In AD 367, the beginning of the end of Roman rule in Britain was signalled by a conspiracy between the Saxon, Pictish and Scottish raiders, which allowed northern and western Britain to pass briefly into barbarian control as the Germanic tribes raided deeply into Gaul. The end came in AD 410 and was preceded by a strategic lapse by the over-stretched imperial command which divided the hitherto effective Channel fleet between Britain and Gaul.

At the time when the Romans were contemplating and completing their conquest of southern Britain a most remarkable type of stronghold was being replicated along the northern coasts. Brochs were cylindrical towers which could stand as tall as 15 m (50 feet). Although no mortar was employed in their construction, the drystone walling was accomplished with outstanding skill and precision. The walls of these towers were built hollow, so that chambers, galleries and stairways could be incorporated between the two skins of stone. The architecture was plainly of a defensive nature, for no window openings were permitted, while doors were small and often opened into a short passageway flanked on either side by guard chambers. Although a few redundant brochs would much later be defended against Viking raiders, the period of broch-building was a short one, spanning the first two or three centuries AD. The brochs remain a mystifying enigma; they may have evolved from fortified circular dwellings of stone and from little Iron Age blockhouses or 'duns', but their sophistication and standardisation are exceptional.

Once, they were regarded as the strongholds of a northern, coast-dwelling race who were in conflict with the Celtic hillfort-dwellers of the Scottish interior. But new archaeological dating techniques revealed that the hillforts were far, far older than the brochs. More than five hundred brochs were built during their brief lifespan, mainly in coastal locations in the north of Scotland, with Orkney and Caithness existing as the heartland of the broch-builders. The best comparisons are probably with the small Scottish tower houses of the medieval and later centuries. Brochs are likely to have been the fortified homes of local chieftains and minor nobles, with each broch controlling a pocket of usable land and a stretch of the coastline. They were built in localities which must always have been impoverished, and the causes for such a heavy expenditure of resources on fortifications are not known. Status and local rivalries may be the answers, though it is conceivable that Roman slaving expeditions might also have encouraged the native people of the wild Scottish shores to invest in defence.

Although their ancestors had been adept and fearsome mariners, the Anglo-Saxons, who gradually formed a dominant minority in England in the centuries after the Roman withdrawal, seem to have lost their prowess as sailors. The first Viking attack appears to have occurred in 789 and to have taken the English completely by surprise. Three ships landed on the isle of Portland and their crews were mistaken for traders, until a royal official rode up to them to claim a toll – and was murdered by the Norse raiders. The raids steadily increased in severity, and in 836 King Egbert led his forces against the crews of some thirty-five Danish ships in a battle at Carhampton, between Watchet and Minehead. He failed to evict the raiders and events took a sinister turn in the 850s when Danish armies wintered in England instead of returning home with their plunder. Ethelwulf had defeated the crews of a formidable armada of 350 Viking ships in 851, and yet the English appeared incapable of preventing the raids. In the 880s, however, Alfred gained the initiative. The chronicles state that he designed a new kind of warship which was swifter, higher and more stable than the longships used by the Vikings. Little is known about the history and organisation of the English navy, though Alfred is thought to have won two naval engagements and to have employed sailors from the Frisian islands, part of the old Anglo-Saxon homeland, to man his ships.

Even so, the main thrust of his strategy to vanquish the Danes was land-based rather than concerned with fleets or coastal forts such as those employed to good effect by the Romans. He and his immediate successors created a series of small, fortified towns or 'burhs' which could serve as defensive nuclei within their respective territories. Most were inland, but a few, such as Wareham, which still preserves its Saxon layout, were seaports.

Later English kings recognised the value of a navy even though their plans were often constrained by the costs involved. In 1008 Ethelred demanded a new fleet, and his kingdom was divided into 'shipsokes', each region being required to furnish a ship of sixty oars, while smaller districts were obliged to donate helmets and corselets for the crews. As a result, he was able to assemble the largest navy that the kingdom had so far possessed at the port of Sandwich. Then some of the gilt was stripped from the naval gingerbread when a disgraced captain embarked on a course of piracy along the southern coast with twenty of the costly vessels and crews. These ships, and the eighty naval vessels which were in hot pursuit, all perished in a great Channel storm, and the vestiges of the briefly glorious navy withdrew to London. Then the Vikings appeared off Sandwich and began a campaign of plundering which ravaged sixteen counties. Eventually they were bribed with the sum of £48,000 to go away.

Cnut was recognised as king in 1017, but although he was a formidable warrior, the bribes of 'Danegeld' and the cost of maintaining naval defences crippled his realm. At the start of his reign

A sea arch forming in the cliffs at Bosherton on the Pembrokeshire coast

Sheer cliffs cut in basalt at Kilt Rock, Skye

A dramatic section of coastline at St Govan's Head in Pembrokeshire

Chalk cliffs and sea stack near Flamborough Head

*Weston Bay and
Weston-super-Mare from
Brean Down*

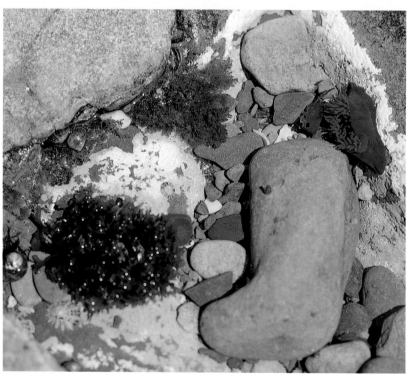

*A corner of a rock pool
with a beadlet anemone*

The colourful shelduck is the most characteristic bird of sand dunes

A barnacle goose

*Eilean Donnan Castle
standing on an islet in
Loch Duich in an area
where Scots and Vikings
fought for control*

*The sea loch of Loch Fyne
near Inverary*

The cliff castle of Gurnard's Head in Cornwall

Part of the Roman defences at the Richborough shore fort

Storm-tossed seas seen from the old stronghold at Tintagel in Cornwall

Edward's great coastal castle at Caernarfon

Wareham, once accessible to sea-going ships

*The view from the fish
wharf at Polperro*

*The Cornish fishing port
of Mevagissey*

The remains of the Norman church built inside the Roman fort of the Saxon shore at Reculver

*Bold cliffs near Lydstep
Head in Pembrokeshire*

*Now, pleasure craft pack
the harbour at St Ives*

The Cuillins seen from the beach at Elgol on Skye

The bizarre Italianate holiday village of Portmerion

Cliffs and a sea stack at Muchalls on the coast of North-east Scotland

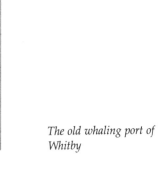

The old whaling port of Whitby

Only pleasure boats
remain at Overy Staithe
in Norfolk

The chalk cliffs at
Bempton

he had forty warships, but by its end in 1035 the navy was reduced to sixteen vessels. Payment of wages to the crews cost England up to £4,000 each year. His successor, Harthacnut, arrived with a force of sixty-two ships to enforce his claim, and then exacted taxes of £21,099 to pay off some of the crews. But thirty-two of the ships were retained in service at a cost of a further £11,048.

In 1049, King Edward disbanded some of the royal ships and the navy was reduced to just five vessels. By 1066, however, it appears that a powerful navy had again been established. By this time the crews included recruits as well as professional sailors. Some ships were provided by the monarch, some by nobles and bishops, some by districts and some by ports. For fifteen days of each year the ports of Dover, Hastings, Hythe, Romney and Sandwich each provided twenty ships manned by twenty-two sailors per vessel. Despite all the earlier expenditure on war fleets, coastal defences played no real part in the events of 1066, for land engagements resulted in the most crushingly successful invasion experienced in the course of English history.

In the September of 1066, Harold took his army into Yorkshire to confront an invasion force led by the Norse Viking, Harald Hardrada, and Harold's own brother, Tostig. Some three hundred Viking ships had been needed to convey the invaders to England, but after the battle of Stamford Bridge only forty-two ships were needed to carry away the defeated survivors. Then news arrived that the host of William of Normandy had made a landfall in the south.

In the May of that year, the English navy had been effective in driving Tostig's raiders from the Isle of Wight. Nevertheless, on 27 September, William loaded an army of about 10,000 men and some 3,000 horses into a fleet of perhaps 700 ships and the next morning the invaders disembarked unopposed at Pevensey with but a couple of ships missing. By crossing the Channel swiftly and mainly at night, the Normans had planned to give the English navy the slip. Otherwise, the heavily laden transports might have been wrecked by what was generally regarded as a formidable and efficient fleet. But winds which had damaged the Norman armada as it moved up the coast from Dives to St Valery in the Somme estuary on 8 September had also damaged the English fleet, which was moved to London, leaving the Sussex invasion coast exposed. Having gained a landfall, there were no fixed coastal defences whatsoever for the Normans to contend with.

The little port of Pevensey (beside the Roman shore fort which had next been manned by a British garrison and had then, so the legends told, been conquered by the Saxon chieftains, Aella and Asa in 491) was at this time located on a narrow peninsula of firm land which projected into a coastal strip of marsh and lagoon running from the Downs eastwards to the busy port of Hastings. A prefabricated defence work was in all likelihood erected inside the tumbling walls of the old Roman fort, but after spending just a day at their bridgehead the invaders probably marched through the coastal marshes along a causeway to Hastings, where the citizens surrendered without fighting. The fleet was then moved to the harbour at Hastings, and William began to ravage the surrounding countryside, hoping to draw Harold's army hastily into battle – whilst at the same time building fortifications to cover his re-embarkation should the English forces prove too strong. The outcome of the Battle of Hastings is known to all, but far fewer realise that if favourable winds had allowed the Norman host to embark for England in mid-August, as intended, the English navy would very likely have severely harried the invading fleet, while Harold's army would certainly have vanquished any forces which landed. The destiny of English history was decided by a combination of bad weather and the Viking landings in the north.

During the Middle Ages, fixed defenceworks, in which the Saxons had shown so little interest, mushroomed and multiplied. Hundreds of castles were built, but very few indeed were conceived as part of a strategy of defence against invasion from across the seas. Many were baronial creations which provided a power-base for a local magnate and a refuge against hostile neighbours. A high proportion were royal castles, built to safeguard the interests of the crown in the provinces, and most of these reflected the preoccupation with internal rather than external threats. But the external threats certainly existed, not only from the Scottish kings and their border barons and the dissident Welsh princes, but also from the continental powers beyond the Channel.

For more than a century after the Norman conquest, the Channel existed virtually as a Norman sea, but at the start of the thirteenth century the English barons, who were in dispute with King John, invited Prince Louis of France to invade. The Cinque Ports of Kent and Sussex refused him entry, but Louis and his forces were landed in Kent by the mercenary, Eustace the Monk, one of the most bizarre figures in medieval history. Eustace then

indulged in piracy amongst the Channel merchant vessels before assembling a large fleet to reinforce the French invaders. It was intercepted by a small English fleet; quicklime was released and driven by the wind into the French crews before the English closed with their arrows and swords. This defeat of the French fleet off Dover and the vanquishing of the baronial faction at Lincoln gave victory to John's heir, the nine-year-old Henry III.

The strategic importance of Dover was recognised in prehistoric times, when a major hillfort was built there during the Iron Age. Within its ramparts the Romans built their lighthouse at an early stage in their occupation and it is almost certain that the hillfort was reused to serve as one of the Saxon burhs. William the Conqueror erected a timber motte and bailey castle here and in the reign of Henry II (1154–89) this was replaced by the splendid stone keep which still survives. This formed the centre-piece for a

Defences of several ages at Dover, with the Norman keep at the top of the picture

137

mighty and elaborate stronghold with an inner curtain wall, ten wall-towers, two double-towered gatehouses and two barbicans. John added an outer curtain wall studded with D-shaped towers. In 1216, however, the weaknesses in the design were exposed when Prince Louis besieged the royal castle and his sappers undermined the northern gateway and brought down its eastern tower. Under Henry III, the ruined gateway was blocked and a new entrance, the Constable's Gate, was built, and the outer curtain wall was extended southward to the head of the cliffs. Used by thousands of visitors each year, Henry's gateway survives as a monument to a seldom-remembered invasion.

During the fourteenth century, the cross-Channel rivalries intensified, with continental piracy on the affluent English wool trade becoming overshadowed by the contest between Edward III of England and Philip VI of France. The conflict resulted in raids, counter-raids and invasions, and while it emphasised the importance of naval power it produced surprisingly little in the way of purpose-built coastal fortifications. In 1338, both Portsmouth and Southampton were plundered and burned by the French. This could have been the opening chapter of a campaign in which Philip would conquer Flanders and then invade England. An army of 20,000 men and a fleet of 200 ships were poised and ready. However, Edward mustered a comparable fleet. and these ships, with their forces of archers, defeated the French at Sluys in 1340 and ended the threat of invasion. The threats of large- and small-scale raids remained, and in 1377 Rye and Hastings were burned, Poole and the Isle of Wight were raided, and attacks on Portsmouth and Southampton were repulsed, although Portsmouth was burned during the skirmishing. In 1416, the Isle of Wight and Portsmouth were blockaded by the French, while in 1473 a French raid on Southampton was intercepted. Brighton and Dover were attacked in 1514.

Coastal castles were common, but even the royal castles were provided to serve a variety of roles, not only being available to serve as defensive nuclei in the event of invasion, but often – and more importantly in the case of some of the greater castles, such as the one at Orford in Suffolk – being sited to assert the royal presence within potentially insurgent territory. Arundel, Bramber, Christchurch, Dover, Eastbourne, Hastings, Lewes, Pevensey, Portchester and Southampton were all fortified posts along the invasion coast, and could call on extra support from garrisons further inland, such as the ones at Canterbury, Abinger,

Bodiam Castle, a private stronghold with a role in national defence

Farnham and Guildford. Bramber controlled any penetration from the valley of the Adur; the Arun valley was dominated by Arundel and Lewes guarded navigation on the river Ouse. Even so, the medieval fortifications did not constitute a coherent and integrated system of defence.

Sometimes private castles were loosely involved in the strategy. In 1385, Sir Edward Dalyngrigge was granted a royal licence to build the beautiful castle at Bodiam in East Sussex. It provided Sir Edward with status and security but it also controlled the Rother valley and guarded Rye, burned in 1377, and New Winchelsea, raided in 1380. Throughout much of the interior, medieval town walls seem to have had more to do with the flaunting of urban status and civic pride and the control of entry to allow the taxation of traders than with the raw necessities of defence. Along the invasion coast, however, walls, gatehouses and towers might rebuff raiding parties which emerged unexpectedly from the marshes. At Rye the Landgate, with its gatehouse towers standing almost 15 m (50 feet) tall, survives. Winchelsea also has a Landgate and at Southampton, the Westgate, Bargate and God's House Gate are preserved.

But the most expensive and sophisticated of the medieval castles in Britain were built by Edward I as a strategy for ringing and stifling the Snowdonia heartland of Welsh independence. These are invaders' castles rather than anti-invasion defences, and most, such as Harlech, Beaumaris and Caernarfon, were designed and

The Welsh castles built by King Edward, like Conwy, could be supplied from the sea in the event of siege

One of the artillery platforms at King Henry VIII's fort at Deal

sited in such ways that they could be supplied by sea in the event of siege.

It was not until the medieval period was almost over that a modern and unified system of coastal forts was created along the invasion coast. In 1545, a continental fleet of 225 ships attacked the English navy as it lay becalmed at Spithead (it was in this engagement that the *Mary Rose* capsized). Then the French retreated, but not before landing a raiding party which caused immense damage on the Isle of Wight. This salutary experience gave further encouragement to the policies by which Henry VIII was seeking to develop a navy of less cumbersome ships and to create a credible and integrated system of fixed anti-invasion defences. The need was a real one, for in 1538 Emperor Charles V and Francis I of France had set aside their differences and combined in an alliance against England's protestant monarch. The key to the strategy lay in the improvement of artillery technology, and in the 1530s new gun foundries were established in the south-east. The fort-building programme spanned the years 1539–47 and involved the introduction of a new type of stronghold: not a refinement of the medieval castle, but forts and blockhouses which would serve primarily as platforms for artillery pieces. The inspiration came from a variety of sources, including the lessons learned from the rather primitive fort built by Henry VII towards the end of the previous century to guard the Dart estuary, continental concepts of fortification, and Henry's own experience of modernising the defences of Calais. The Henrician coastal forts were each individually designed, but they were both similar and original in that they constituted a coherent system for coastal defence and concentrated a formidable mass of firepower on structures which were compact and very strong.

At first, it was hoped that the coast could be armoured all the way from Hull to the south of Wales, but in the event the forts were established along the traditional invasion coast, from the blockhouses guarding the Thames estuary at Tilbury to the fortresses of Pendennis and St Mawes in the west, which controlled the approaches to Falmouth. The finest expression of the new ideas was created at Deal, the key fort in the complex of strongholds guarding the vulnerable coast flanking the Downs. A central cylindrical tower was clasped by six half-round bastions, and it rose a storey higher than the two-storey bastions around it. Its summit, and those of the bastions, provided platforms for artillery pieces which could together engage forces approaching from land or sea. Great care was taken to protect the fort against conquest by troops landed nearby and attempting to take it from the rear, for the artillery fort was surrounded by a formidable moat, and low-level gunports were provided to allow a murderous fire to sweep attackers from this moat.

Each fort was rather different; the one at St Mawes had three bastions clasping its tower in a cloverleaf pattern, that at Walmer had four, while Pendennis had a circular gun emplacement which was concentric to its tower. Moving around the invasion coast, forts or the smaller blockhouses were installed at Tilbury, Gravesend, Sandown, Deal, Walmer, Dover, Sandgate, Camber, Southsea, Calshot, Hurst, Yarmouth and the approaches to Cowes on the Isle of Wight, Brownsea Island, Sandsfoot, Weymouth and Falmouth. Some of these forts have been lost, including Sandown fort, which was washed away by the sea, but others, such as Deal and St Mawes, still provide an impressive testimony to the stark might of their design.

Whether the excellence of this complex of defences had any bearing on the fact that it was not put to the test, we do not know. The system certainly owed more to pragmatic necessity than to any more philosophical reasoning. Nevertheless it did reflect an important change in political outlook. During the Tudor period a sense of English (if not English-plus-Welsh) identity was developing. Previously, nationalism had had a very low profile indeed.

Soldiers fought for money or because they were obliged to fight by their feudal superiors – only seldom did they fight for national causes. Kings were generally, but not always, more preoccupied with the machinations of their own barons than with the designs of hostile monarchs, while the Roman Catholic church had existed as a great international institution. England and France were the first kingdoms to discover identities as nation states. But once the nation state had come into being, then the prime obligation of government became the defence of the nation and the protection of the inviolable nature of the sovereign territory. So long as it was possible for any invasion to be repelled in the Channel or upon the beaches, the maintenance of a fleet and a credible network of fixed coastal defences would have the highest priority.

An invasion early-warning system based on hill-top beacons was occasionally activated during the Middle Ages, and a more effective network of beacons was established in 1585 – in time to warn of the approach of the Spanish Armada in 1588. Already, new forts had been added to the Henrician complex to defend Tresco in the Scilly Isles, and at Upnor, to guard the fleet in the Medway. Queen Elizabeth and Queen Mary both invested huge sums in the fortification of Berwick-on-Tweed, England's frontier outpost against Scottish invasion. The invasion fears associated with the Spanish Armada were sufficient to ensure that the need for coastal defences were not forgotten, but another reminder, if it was needed, was provided in 1667, when a Dutch fleet penetrated the Medway defences, burned sixteen ships and wasted Chatham dockyard. This inspired a new campaign of coastal fortification which focused on defending the bases from which the navy operated. Plymouth, the Medway and Tilbury all gained massive and costly defences.

By the time of Henry VIII, naval guns had become formidable weapons – which now posed more of a threat to their targets than to their operators. Yet right up until the time of the Spanish Armada, the nature of naval warfare was still debated, and many commanders still regarded ships primarily as mobile fighting platforms for infantry. The naval strategy of Tudor, Elizabethan and later times envisaged great duels between foreign fleets and the English coastal defences. It might have been argued that, since England now possessed a very powerful navy, any invaders could be defeated at sea, making fixed coastal defences unnecessary. However, in the days of sail, a fleet's freedom of movement was greatly restricted by the direction of the prevailing wind, while at any particular time, flotillas could be dispersed to accomplish different tasks in different parts of the world. Fixed defences were much more predictable and reliable, even though they could only engage in defensive warfare and could not actually inflict a defeat on enemy vessels, which always retained the option of sailing out of range of the shore-mounted guns.

As the years rolled by and the catalogue of invasion scares lengthened, so the power of naval guns increased and the coastal defences became more numerous and more heavily armoured. Naval firepower was impressive, and at the time of the Napoleonic wars in the early nineteenth century, a fleet of ten ships of the line, each firing broadsides, could launch some five hundred missiles at a shore fort within a matter of a few minutes. If working at the limit of the range of its guns then the accuracy of the fire from such a fleet would suffer, though by sailing into and out of the range of the shore artillery the raids could be repeated with modest risks unless the defending fleet intervened. Given the escalation in armaments, one might have expected that the shore defences would have become ever more massive and sophisticated, but there was an important exception to this trend. In 1783 a tower on the Corsican coast was shelled by two British frigates, but the bombardment was seen to have caused remarkably little destruction. A year later the exercise was repeated, but again the structure seemed immune to modern gunnery, although the barrage which it returned set a frigate on fire and killed a large number of crew. In the end, the stone tower was reduced, but only after batteries firing red-hot shot had been landed on the shore. Here, apparently, was something worth imitating.

The tower was on the Cap Mortella, stood 12 m (40 feet) tall, was 14 m (45 feet) in diameter and had walls 4 m (13 feet) thick. The English imitations hence became known as Martello towers; seventy-four examples were built to guard the invasion coast of south-eastern England and a total of 150 Martello towers were built, some appearing at colonial outposts in Canada and South Africa. The towers varied in their dimensions, some being as tall as, and far broader than their original, while others were much smaller. Cylindrical forms were favoured and were built two storeys tall, with their entrances placed at upper-storey level, and accessible only by ladder or drawbridge. The vaulted rooms inside the towers housed garrisons which could resist attackers and the summits served as platforms for two or three artillery pieces. Most of the towers were moated. Obviously they did not represent any great advance in sophistication on the Tudor forts, and were similar to them in many respects.

Another defencework of a backward-looking type was the Royal Military Canal. Some 37 km (23 miles) in length and running from Hythe to Rye, the canal was dug to provide a defensible perimeter to the Dungeness–Romney Marsh area. No less than 180 guns were provided to fortify the line. The canal isolated the presumed landing ground for an invasion fleet which, it was feared, Napoleon was assembling in Boulogne. The fears arose in 1803, and by the time that the canal was completed, in 1809, any threat of invasion had, for the time being, vanished.

In 1837, the first shell-firing guns were adopted by the French navy; in 1843, the Americans launched the first screw-driven steamship; during the American Civil War of the 1860s there was the first duel between ironclads, one equipped with a rotating gun turret, and the first successful submarine mission. Factors such as these all urged a revision of coastal defence strategy, but the most startling revelation came in 1858, when a British committee deduced that France, with its new ironclads, had quietly achieved a naval superiority in Channel waters. Once more the debate raged over whether Britain would be adequately guarded by a fleet of roving artillery platforms or whether the key ports needed fixed shore defences. In 1860, a Royal Commission was appointed to tackle the problem, and in the course of the years which followed new forts, which were capable of resisting assaults by forces of marines, were established along the invasion coast. The Thames, Medway, Milford Haven and Solent estuaries were all refortified. Around Plymouth and Portsmouth self-contained fortresses-cum-barracks were built according to the latest principles of military engineering, and were armed with heavy guns in shell-proof casements. In the Solent four circular forts, armoured in iron, rose sheer from the sea to guard Portsmouth harbour. The high ground of Portsdown Hill, which overlooked Portsmouth, was also fortified with four great and three minor forts to prevent the hill being used as a platform for the reduction of the port below. The forts in Milford Haven also rose straight from the water, with the exception of the one on Stack Rock, which was placed on a rocky islet. In the 1870s, Plymouth and Chatham were similarly ringed by forts.

Whether or not the threat which inspired all this defensive fervour had any reality, the sums invested in stone, concrete and iron were enormous. The largest of the Solent forts was completed in 1880 at what was then the staggering cost of £242,000. The Royal Commission forts, though never tested in war, were formidable and advanced in the detail of their design. But even so, they embodied the same military doctrine which had been enshrined in King Henry VIII's coastal forts. They housed soldiers who were free to advance against invaders but secure from their attack, and they existed as platforms mounting artillery which could be ranged against ships or forces engaged in attacking strategic objectives along the invasion coast.

Thereafter, military thinking had to change. Firstly the Zeppelins and then the Gotha bomber raids during the 1914–18 war signalled that the nature of warfare had changed. The sovereign nation state could no longer sit secure behind its fleet and within its fixed coastal defences. A new turn in the spiral of horror of warfare now made it possible for the civilian population of the 'soft' interior to be placed in the front line of conflict by any adversary gaining a superiority in air power. This form of power had to be added to the defensive equation. The relative strengths and weaknesses of air and sea power had to be assessed. Advanced airfields were needed to control coastal shipping, and early-warning systems were needed to detect raiders: raiders advancing at more than twelve times the speed of the fastest destroyer and capable of flying over the heaviest concentration of artillery. Tank traps, minefields, barbed wire entanglements and pill boxes festooned the invasion coast, but if coastal defences were essential and credible in 1940, within a couple of decades they were shown to be as irrelevant to the horrors of modern conflict as an Elizabethan fire ship or as quicklime cast into the breeze. By the time that coastal armour became obsolete the most threatened coasts of the British seaboard had acquired a remarkable legacy of military archaeology.

Medieval castles stand inside Iron Age hillforts or Roman forts of the Saxon shore, and from their crumbling towers there are views of Henrician block-houses, Napoleonic Martello towers or the relics of several other ages of fear. Few of these expensive strongholds were ever actually put to the test. Is this a testimony to their excellence as deterrents or to the xenophobic paranoia of their builders? One can argue about this, but who could argue with the contention that the invasion coast of south-eastern England has a legacy of military architecture quite unrivalled in its diversity?

Chapter Seven

THE UNCARING SEA

'I will never happen to us': this seems to have been the motto of so many little communities as they set out to establish their roots in a coastal setting. Where Nature is concerned, mankind seems to have a peculiar capacity for ignoring the lessons of the past. And yet most coastlines are quite regularly punctuated by examples of lost, marooned and withered settlements which failed because their founders underestimated the power of waves, currents or landslips. They seem to have regarded the coast as a line on the map which was fixed for all time, when in fact any coastline simply represents a brief stage in the contest between land and sea or a geological snapshot of the state of play between the forces of erosion and deposition.

Some settlements were blessed with stability, so that Dover has been a thriving harbour since prehistoric times. In other places, the transitional nature of the coastline has been heavily emphasised. An early Bronze Age axe-hammer tool has been dredged up from a site which is now some 8 km (5 miles) off the Norfolk coast, and in this county the soft cliffs which lie between Weybourne and the Broads have retreated about 5 km (about 3 miles) since Roman times, and between 1 m and 4.5 m (1 and 5 yards) of land are still being lost here each year.

For some residents, the death of a coastal settlement involved a sudden awakening and a dash through the night, scrambling on cliff tracks lashed by rain and turning to see the old homesteads slumping and consumed by the sea. In other places, there was no sudden death, only a creeping decay as invisible banks of silt rose to choke the harbour channel, while warehouses stood empty and merchants moved their vessels to rival ports. The decline of one port could indeed spell success for its neighbour, and on some stretches of coast the baton of success was passed from one harbour to another as Nature toyed with the pawns on her chessboard. In the fourteenth century the River Blyth cut a new outlet to the sea and the harbour at the great Suffolk seaport of Dunwich began to choke. Walberswick, sited on the new mouth of the river, captured some of the trade from its crumbling neighbour and enjoyed a spell of prosperity, before it too faced decline during the Commonwealth. Not far away is Southwold, which flourished and expanded rapidly in the sixteenth century, but it had been a

The crumbling East Anglian coast at Covehithe

The lost town of Dunwich lay to seaward of these retreating cliffs

borough for only eighty-five years when, in 1590, a new channel had to be dredged through the shingle banks which were choking its harbour. Nearby is Blythburgh, which also decayed in the seventeenth century, when the little estuarine port seems to have been at war with all the elements, for a series of fires added to the damage caused by the offshore currents.

Dunwich is the most famous name on the long list of coastal casualties. This Suffolk port was one of the leading towns in Saxon England and was important in Norman East Anglia long before it purchased its charter from King John. In 1235, its prosperity was marked by the thirty vessels which it made available for the fleet of Henry III. The harbour sheltered trading ships and fishing boats; merchants had their houses and warehouses here, and there was even a mint. During the thirteenth century Dunwich was a rival to the other great East Anglian seaports of Great Yarmouth and Lowestoft. It had eight or nine parish churches, two friaries, a hospital and a preceptory of the Knights Templar. Markets were held on every day of the week.

The beginning of the borough's prolonged decline was signalled in the March of 1286, when winds from the east drove the high spring tide against the shore and its soft, slithery cliffs. Houses, barns and two parish churches were toppled, while later in the century another gale-driven tide accounted for the harbour and three more churches. Then the harbour began to choke with the silt from the Blyth. By the end of the Middle Ages, these natural disasters had obliterated most of the features in the old town plan, and the final indignity came in 1677, when the sea penetrated the old market place. Early in the next century, Daniel Defoe found that Dunwich was still attempting to trade, and was shipping out locally produced butter, cheese and corn, although this small-scale commerce was really the last gasp of a once great seaport. He observed that: 'for once they had fifty churches in the town; I saw but one left, and that not half full of people.' But he knew that Dunwich was not unique, for he had just arrived from Orford, which he also described: 'Orford was once a good town, but it is decayed, and as it stands on the land-side of the river, the sea daily throws up more land to it, and falls off itself from it, as if it was resolved to disown the place, and that it should be a sea port no longer.'

It was the growth of the spit of Orford Ness which reduced the fortunes of this promising medieval port. When Henry II built his castle here in 1162, to assert his control of the surrounding province, the town was flourishing and the spit seems to have been stable; it extended for just a mile southwards from Orford and provided useful protection to vessels in the harbour and shelter from storms from the north-east. In Elizabethan times, Orford became a free borough and still retained a fishing fleet, but soon the lengthening of Orford Ness would suffocate the commerce of the town which it sheltered. By the eighteenth century, this had taken place, and the waters behind the spit were only used by ships sheltering from storms at sea. The townlet existed as a rotten borough until it was disenfranchised in 1832. Now the spit runs parallel to the coast for some 18 km (11 miles) and Orford is, like its castle, only a picturesque fossil.

During the historical period the most dramatic changes have been those affecting the south-eastern coast. As we have seen, in Roman times the geography of this coast was much different from that of today. The Wantsum Channel separated the Isle of Thanet from the mainland, and this channel was used by vessels seeking to round the promontory of Kent while avoiding the hazards of the Goodwin Sands. Further along the coast, just to the south-west of the North Downs, the Romney Marsh existed as a deep embayment in the coast which yielded, in the area where we now find the shingle headland of Dungeness, to a complex of sand banks, mud-flats and creeks. In the centuries which followed, land was reclaimed by man as the sea played its own role in reshaping the coastline, while in 1287, a sea storm destroyed much that had accrued from the patient efforts of drain digging and sea-wall building during the three or four preceding centuries. Storms such as this marked the end of an era of reclamation which had also seen land won from the sea on the northern flanks of the Humber estuary and the Pevensey Levels in Sussex.

Meanwhile, communities of seafarers and merchants had developed – and their interests were not always in tune with those of the people engaged in reclaiming the land and redefining the coast. The medieval Cinque Ports – originally Dover, Hastings, Hythe, Romney and Sandwich – and Ancient Ports, such as Winchelsea and Rye, spearheaded both the merchant and naval divisions of English shipping. They enjoyed privileged positions, being exempt from customs duties, having the right to salvage cargoes from wrecked vessels, and even being granted the right to carry out acts of piracy. But in return, they each provided a quota of ships which formed the backbone of the king's navy. Gradually, however, the changes to the coast and the silting of channels reversed the fortunes of many of these proud ports. When Defoe visited Sandwich early in the eighteenth century he found: 'an old, decayed, poor, miserable town, of which when I have said that it is an ancient town, one of the Cinque Ports, and sends two members to Parliament; I have said all that I think can be worth anybody's reading of the town of Sandwich.' And today, of all the Cinque and Ancient Ports which stood with their toes in the sea, only Hastings, Hythe and Dover still stand beside the sea.

Perhaps the most fascinating of the tales of misfortune are those concerning the Winchelseas, already mentioned. Old Winchelsea stood on the eastern side of the channels that formed the mouth of the river Brede. It began to be affected by storm damage in 1244,

One of the dwellings at the sand-entombed Neolithic village of Skara Brae

but the port was too valuable to be sacrificed and in 1280 Edward I decided to resite its community. He acquired the nearby manor of Iham and gave his agents a period of three years in which to lay out a new borough. In accordance with current thinking on town planning, New Winchelsea was designed with a gridwork of streets which divided the town plan into numerous 'quarters'. The plan called for some thirty-nine quarters, two churches, a market, a friary and stone defences. In the event, however, the full vision did not materialise and burgesses were not enticed in the expected numbers. Many merchants remained stubbornly in the old town, leaving only in 1287, when violent storms changed the course of the river Rother, destroyed the harbour at New Romney, and brought Old Winchelsea to a violent end. At the end of the thirteenth century work began on building walls to defend the perimeter of the new town, but this work was never finished. It coincided with a brief burst of prosperity, but this was not sustained and the work on building the church of St Thomas began with an over-ambitious chancel and scarcely progressed any further. During the fourteenth century some larger gaps in the pattern of urban prosperity began to appear as repeated French raiding and burning combined with the ravages of the Black Death to sap the spirits of the townspeople. Even so, in 1369 New

153

Winchelsea contained more than 375 inhabited houses, although by the end of the Middle Ages such dwellings may only have numbered around fifty. By this time, Nature had sided with the other adversaries, for the sea had retreated and the estuary which gave the town its access to the maritime world was choked with silt. The decline continued, so that by the middle of the eighteenth century New Winchelsea was greatly reduced, and twenty-seven of the original thirty-nine quarters were abandoned to grass and weeds. Defoe had already described it most aptly as the skeleton of an ancient city. Today the geometry created by Edward's planners survives in the townscape and the surrounding fieldscape. Dwellings still stand on a dozen quarters around the surviving church, but the atmosphere is genteel and soulful and the bustle departed long ago.

While some once prosperous places faced a slow suffocation as their links with the sea were stifled by silt and sand, others met a more dramatic fate. Very few people have heard of Ravenserodd, but it was an important port for a part of the Middle Ages. It was at the mouth of the Humber about 3 km (2 miles) to the north of the present position of the tip of Spurn Head. Close to it was Ravenser, which appears to have begun as a Danish anchorage and was the port of departure for Hardrada's defeated and depleted host in 1066. Thereafter Ravenser may have stagnated, but it gained some substance during the thirteenth century, when it was hauled into prominence through its association with a successful neighbour. In about 1241 the Count of Aumale built the town of Odd, which soon became known as Ravenserodd, nearby on an island of sand and stones. The old records tell that around 1235 the waves and currents of the North Sea were casting up banks of sand and shingle at the tip of the medieval Spurn peninsula (which was then in a more westerly position). A man gathered driftwood, the timbers from a ship wrecked on the spit, and built his hut here, where he lived by selling meat and drink to passing mariners. This humble habitation and enterprise formed the nucleus for the Count's new town. In the middle of the century, Odd was granted a weekly market and a fair of sixteen days; by the 1260s it supported more than a hundred townspeople, many of them trading in herrings, and at the end of the century it became a free borough with two more markets and a fair lasting thirty days. And yet its only link with the mainland to the north was a sandy track along the spit which was said to be 'no broader than an arrow's flight'. The new town flourished as a commercial centre, while Ravenser, its partner, served as a port. The towns were sufficiently important to be called upon to furnish ships for royal campaigns, and they engaged in fierce competition with other Humber ports, such as Grimsby.

By the middle of the next century, however, the fortunes of the towns named after the raven had been reversed. Perhaps as early as 1256, when there was a great sea storm, the narrow natural causeway to the mainland was breached and Ravenserodd became an island. It survived this setback, but in 1346 the sea invaded and two-thirds of the town were swept away. In 1347–8, Edward III instructed his tax collectors to reduce the burden of taxation, for he had learned that Ravenserodd was being inundated by the sea, its foundations and dwellings washed away. One landlord alone had lost some 145 buildings there, while 'the persons now dwelling there are so impoverished that they are not able in any way to support or pay the tenths and tolls, taxations, etc'. The chronicler of Meaux Abbey described the urgency of the evacuation: 'All men daily removing their possessions, the town was swiftly swallowed up and irreparably destroyed by merciless floods and tempests.' A couple of years later the tides were exhuming bodies in the churchyard, and in 1355 those that still remained were disinterred and reburied at Easington. By the end of the century, Ravenserodd was almost completely washed away and all that remained at Ravenser was the manor house. Now they are both lost and submerged somewhere on the estuary side of the great spit which terminates at Spurn Head.

Meanwhile, floods had threatened land and villages a few miles away on the northern shores of the Humber estuary. During the more optimistic years of the earlier medieval centuries, this had been the scene of great land reclamation schemes, some carried out by laymen and some by the Cistercian monks of Meaux Abbey, nearby. Towards the end of the thirteenth century, the climate began to take on the angry character which would threaten so many coastal places during the following century. In the south-east of Holderness, the northern shores of the Humber estuary extended about 3 kilometres (about 2 miles) further south than today, and here great flocks of sheep grazed the coastal pastures around the villages of Sunthorp and Orwithfleet. During the 1320s, however, the sea washed over these grazings and both villages were obliterated. To the west of these lost places and to the south of Otteringham lay Sunk Island, which exists as low-lying land today. Three villages here were lost when the island

A chapel engulfed by shifting sand dunes on the Welsh coast at Llandanwg

was submerged for a long period from about the fifteenth to the seventeenth century. The monks of Meaux, who had striven so hard to reclaim pastures here, now struggled to repair their floodbanks. Reduced and debilitated by the Black Death, they struggled in vain, and in 1400 they stood helplessly by as their grange at the doomed village of Tharlesthorp was swept away.

Earlier I described how a whole host of villages and hamlets has been washed from the eroding coast of Holderness, while disasters were not unknown on the less vulnerable Yorkshire coast further north. Some took place long after the storm-ridden times of the later Middle Ages. Runswick Bay is a picturesque village of holiday homes and Victorian villas – but this is not the original settlement. The old village had a perilous position at the foot of the unstable cliff and on one night, in 1664, it slithered into the sea and just a single dwelling survived. Most of the inhabitants escaped, although their adventures were less dramatic than those which would be shared by the people of nearby Kettleness. At the start of the nineteenth century this was a substantial village, which prospered from its alum-working industry. Then, during a December storm in 1829, the cliff which supported the village and its alum works crumbled. The villagers, unable to scrabble up the shifting, slumping slopes, looked seawards for salvation and some of them found refuge on an alum boat which was moored offshore.

In the course of countless centuries settlements were swept from their cliff-foot perches, robbed of their commerce as sand choked their harbours or were nibbled away by the encroaching tides. There were others still which were engulfed and buried as coastal dunes advanced. This happened at all stages in the colonisation of Britain, and at Skara Brae on Orkney, as we have mentioned, it resulted in the entombment and preservation of one of the earliest and most fascinating village sites yet to be discovered in Europe. At Sands of Forvie, near the Ythan estuary and to the north of Aberdeen, archaeologists have explored the remains of an early Iron Age village of hunters, fishers and pastoralists which surrendered to the footloose dunes. Close by there are the stone footings of the Dark Age church which served the village of Forvie for centuries until it met its end in 1413, when gales caused the dunes to march across its site. Even more striking is the half-buried Welsh church which projects from the encroaching sands at Llandanwg in the coastal dune belt between Barmouth Bay and Tremadog Bay.

In Wales there is no saga of misfortune to outstrip that which concerns Kenfig in West Glamorgan. The current village dates only from the sixteenth century, but to its west a medieval town lies buried, marked by sections of its castle walls which emerge from the dunes. People settled here and hereabouts from Stone Age times, and a minor Welsh ruler had his castle at Kenfig in Norman times. Early in the twelfth century, a planned borough was created here by the English, and was ringed by an earth and timber palisade. Better defences soon followed, with the construction of a strong castle of stone. Then a long sequence of fierce Welsh attacks on the alien plantation town was set in motion in 1167, when the young borough was completely destroyed. Kenfig was rebuilt, and four or five severe assaults were survived before the next century had run its course. Yet despite these hardships, it supported 142 households of townsfolk in 1307; the households were reduced to 100 by an attack by Llywelyn Bren in 1316, but by 1349 Kenfig was home to 144 families of burgesses, and its total population must have amounted to around 700–800 souls. Plainly,

The planned outline of the medieval town of Winchelsea

one needed to be made in a stern mould to endure life in this dangerous frontier region and the folk of Kenfig were obviously resolute and durable.

During the next century, however, no amount of resolve could prove equal to the new challenges faced. Sand encroached across the townscape and, by 1471, when the church was made redundant, Kenfig had become almost deserted. Some people moved away completely, others shifted to a new village established nearby to the east. When the chronicler, Leland, came here in the 1530s he saw just this village and 'a Castel, both in ruines and almost chokid and devoured with the Sandes that the Severne Se there castith up'. The last family found living at Kenfig, amongst the partly entombed ruins of the castle, was recorded in 1665. The sands from the Severn sea which bury medieval Kenfig are too deep to make wholesale excavation a prospect for the forseeable future, but one day archaeologists may have the resources and techniques necessary to reveal the unadulterated remains of a lost medieval town, and the information still preserved must be priceless.*

* Information on Kenfig from Ian Soulsby, *The Towns of Medieval Wales*, Phillimore, 1983.

Chapter Eight

PORTS AND RESORTS

Seaside towns are found at short intervals around most of the British coast. Some are old and some are young; some are fishing ports, some resorts and some trading ports, while some began as one thing and have become another. In many cases, the early history is known only in the most sketchy manner, though in many others growth was not spontaneous and haphazard, for the places concerned were deliberate creations and were set out according to precise principles of planning. All have sampled the opportunities and hazards of a coastal situation, while plenty have flourished or failed because of the intervention of factors quite unrelated to their immediate surroundings – including the layout of the national railway network and the rise of new fashions in recreation. Many a seedy and failing fishing village was propelled into urban stardom after being discovered by Victorian artists, bathers and holidaymakers. Each port and resort has its own story of good luck, bad luck and local entrepreneurship. A whole set of volumes would be needed just to outline each story if all the facts were to be told. Generally, however, much still remains to be discovered, and in the space available here one can only describe a few examples which seem to reflect a fair cross section of coastal history.

As we have already seen, some ports, such as Dover and London, have flourished since earliest times, while we know of several ports which were important in medieval times but which are now vanished or redundant, including Dunwich, Ravenser and Sandwich, already described. Sometimes the growth of a port was inevitable in a spot which Nature had endowed with deep and sheltered anchorages and good routeways to a productive interior. The emergence of a port was not always simply determined by the blessings of natural advantage, and some of the places which have the best-documented history were deliberate creations which were born in the minds of influential men. New Winchelsea and Ravenserodd are good examples, as we have seen, but a more fortunate and famous one is Kingston-upon-Hull.

The town began its life under the less prestigious name of Wyke, and it was a little port established at the confluence of the Hull and Humber by the monks of Meaux Abbey during the third quarter of the twelfth century. Wyke was a planned medieval town like New Winchelsea, it had a grid pattern of streets and stood beside the Hull, which was diverted into a new and straight canalised course. Wyke exported the agricultural produce of its

Small fishing craft at anchor at Portree on Skye

East Riding hinterland, most notably wool, and rose to become one of the top six English seaports. This does not mean that it was comparable to modern Bristol or even modern Bognor, for in 1293 when Edward I purchased the manor containing the port Wyke still had only fifty-five occupied tenements.

Edward had acted in order to improve the port facilities at what now became quite literally the Kingston-upon-Hull. He enlarged the quay, established a mint, extended the markets and fairs and improved the approach roads from York and Beverley. Extra incentives for merchants to settle here arrived in 1299, when the townspeople were given their borough charter and freedom from tolls throughout the kingdom. During the following century, Hull flourished, and it acquired a unique and distinctive townscape. The burgesses ringed their town in a massive, towered wall and gained an enormous church – all this work was accomplished in brick, a material which had been almost totally neglected since Roman times. By the middle of the fourteenth century, almost every space within this girdle of walls was packed with dwellings and commercial premises, and the fruits of royal patronage were obvious. Most successful towns owe much to home-grown entrepreneurs, and Hull produced the De la Pole brothers, the most affluent and perceptive speculators and money-lenders in the kingdom. Yet such good fortune could not protect Hull from the effects of more general forces, and as the Hanseatic League of northern European trading ports expanded its influence, so the merchants of Hull found themselves barred from the Baltic ports, and in the second half of the fifteenth century, Hull entered a deep recession.

The town stagnated, and even by the middle of the seventeenth century it had failed to expand beyond the confines of its three-centuries-old walls, within which there were now plenty of undeveloped sites. During the next century, however, the port began to grow again, and by 1700 the walled area had become badly congested. When Defoe visited Hull early in the eighteenth century, he found it serving as an outlet for Derbyshire lead and the butter, cheese and corn of Yorkshire and the north Midlands, and he praised the honesty of the Hull merchants. The Baltic trade had recovered, and as well as handling imports from the Baltic, Hull was also shipping in wine, oil and fruit from France and Spain and tobacco and sugar from the West Indies. However, he feared that the town was vulnerable to bombardment from the sea, and thought that congestion brought other risks: 'The town is exceeding close built, and should a fire ever be its fate, it might suffer deeply on that account; 'tis extraordinary populous, even to an inconvenience, having really no room to extend it self by buildings.' This congestion increased to an insufferable degree, for in the century following Defoe's visit, Hull's population increased sixfold. In the second half of the eighteenth century the town burst the girdle of its medieval walls, and these were destroyed in the course of the building of new docks. By the end of the century, Hull ranked fourth in England after the three much larger ports of London, Liverpool and Bristol.

Few places could match the good fortune of Hull, and it was generally the case that success for one port was enjoyed at the expense of its neighbours. The triumph of Hull suppressed the commerce of its competitors beside the Humber: Patrington, Hedon and Ravenserodd. Patrington never amounted to very much as a trading port, Ravenserodd we have already visited, while Hedon was founded on high hopes which were not fulfilled. Hedon was created by the Counts of Aumale, who would also found Odd, during the first half of the twelfth century. It was not a seaside town, but enjoyed access to the Humber via a narrow creek, the Hedon Haven. The town was built to a geometrical grid plan within the confines of a square boundary ditch, and enjoyed a measure of success from its trade in wool and hides. It had three churches and half a mile of harbour frontage divided between three docks. Not far away, however, lay the growing port of Hull, which was blessed with royal patronage. At the start of the thirteenth century, Hedon ranked eleventh on the list of English ports, but soon it was to suffer in competition with its Humber rivals. Then the outlet to the Humber began to silt, and the merchants of Hedon seem to have attempted to overcome this hardship by trying to move the population of the village at Paull Holme to Paull Fleet at the mouth of the Hedon, where it was hoped that a new out-port for Hedon could take root.

But by 1476, it was plain that these hopes were doomed, and two of Hedon's churches fell into disuse. Apparently the hopes were not entirely extinguished; Defoe found Hedon a pleasant little town and: 'having a little haven from the sea, which threatens Hull, that it will in time grow up to be a great place, for it indeed increases daily; but I fear for them, that their haven will do nothing considerable for them, unless they can do something very considerable for that. They tell us at Headon, that the sea encroaches upon the land on all that shore, and that there are

*The stranded medieval
port of Hedon*

many large fields quite eaten up; that several towns were formerly known to be there, which are now lost; from whence they may suppose, that as the sea by encroachment had damnified their harbour, so if it grows upon them a little more they shall stand open to the sea, and so need no harbour at all, or make a mole, as 'tis called abroad, and have a good road without it. But this is a view something remote.' Today, Hedon is just a third as large as it was in its medieval heyday, but as a result of its failure to grow and evolve, the visitor will find its medieval layout preserved intact.

At ports or former ports like Hedon and New Winchelsea misfortune conserved the vision of the medieval founders, while in places such as Hull we know that the origins were also deliberate and coherent even though success and expansion would erase the outlines of medieval planning. But there were many other ports where the growth was gradual and much more complicated, and the origins less certain. Aberdeen is the most northerly university town in Britain, and right through until the middle of this century one could have moved westward along a line of latitude and have proceeded almost all the way around the world before finding, in Leningrad, a larger and more northerly city. With its great harbour and a distinctive urban character endowed by the locally quarried grey granite, Aberdeen seems to be a coherent entity, but in fact it is the product of a merging together of two towns. The great rivers, the Dee and the Don, almost converge on the North Sea at Aberdeen. At the mouth of the Don, Old Aberdeen developed in Norman times as an ecclesiastical centre near St Machar's cathedral, while at the mouth of the Dee the New Town, a seaport and commercial centre, expanded. The divisions between the two communities survived through the Middle Ages; in 1495 a university was established in Old Aberdeen, and in 1593 Marischal College was established just a mile away as a rival, Protestant university in the New Town. The two universities did not merge until 1860.

At Great Yarmouth a very old layout survived until most of it was destroyed by bombing during the Second World War. The town has its origins in Saxon times, when a fishing community became established on offshore sand banks, and it was not until 1347 that silting linked the island to the mainland. Yarmouth may have begun as the seasonal base of farmer-fishermen who would occupy huts on the bank when the herring shoaled in the autumn, but by the Norman Conquest it had grown into a busy little town of more than 400 people, including the families of twenty-four fishermen. The town, as it developed in the earlier medieval centuries, had five main streets which ran from north to south, and these were cut across by some 156 narrow alleyways, 'The Rows'. These alleys seem to have led to net-drying grounds on the sandy beaches on the eastern flanks of the spit, and it may have been that as the river Yare gradually silted and shifted westwards, so the alleys lengthened as the townsfolk colonised new land, while some of the main streets could have followed the margins of successive shorelines. It has also been suggested that the building of the narrow alleys could have represented an attempt to dispel the effects of sand-laden onshore winds, which were forever raising the height of the sand bank and choking the streets. Despite its island situation, Great Yarmouth flourished; its fishing fleet harvested the North Sea herring shoals and its merchants and mariners traded in East Anglian worsted cloth. Meanwhile, the East Anglian ports engaged in a competition with their more southerly equivalents which went far beyond the bounds of commercial rivalry. Piracy was commonplace, and the sailors of Yarmouth were frequently at war with those of the Cinque Ports, as well as with those of their close neighbour, Gorleston on Sea. Towards the end of the thirteenth century, the town gained an impressive circuit of towered walls.

The roots of the animosity between Yarmouth and the Cinque Ports seem to go back to 1278, when Edward I granted a Royal Charter to the south coast ports. Among the other provisions, he granted the rights of 'Den and Strond' at Yarmouth. This allowed the southerners to land without paying a fee at Yarmouth, to sell their fish there and dry their nets on the strand, while they were also given control of the Yarmouth herring fair. The Norfolk fishermen deeply resented these intrusions. According to the Chronicle of Matthew Paris, however, the antagonism was already well established. He records that in 1254 the people of Winchelsea provided some ships to ferry Queen Eleanor to the continent, but the Yarmouth community made a far more handsome ship available to transport Prince Edward. Furious with jealousy, the Portsmen 'treacherously and suddenly made an attack on it, destroying the ship, and wounding and slaying some of the crew; and in order to palliate their crime, they took the mast of the destroyed vessel, and fitted it to the queen's ship as though they had acted as they did for her benefit and advantage.' This feud plumbed the depths of its stupidity in 1297, when Edward's navy was mustering to face the French fleet. As soon as the Yarmouth vessels came into view, the sailors from the Cinque Ports forgot all about the French, turned about and sank thirty-two of the Norfolk ships and killed two hundred crew. The king ordered that in future the ships from the rival ports should remain well apart, but the feud rumbled on. The Portsmen were usually in the wrong, but they knew that the monarchs relied upon their boats to defend the most vulnerable sections of the invasion coast, and would be loath to act against them.

Other places positively thrived on piracy. During the earlier part of the Middle Ages, before trade links with Brittany and Gascony were fully developed, the little ports of Cornwall and Devon tended to suffer in competition with the Channel ports, which were better placed to trade in the products of the English heartlands. Some western ports, Fowey in particular, developed a specialisation in piracy. This lasted through the Middle Ages, and

in the 1530s the chronicler, Leland, found Fowey 'waxing rich, partly by feats of war, partly by piracy'. Fowey had begun to form in the middle of the twelfth century, after the marriage between Henry II and Eleanor of Aquitaine led to a strengthening of links between England and the south-west of France. It lay near the mouth of its river, and as it grew, so streets parallel to the waterfront colonised the hillside.

Poole was another roost for pirates. In Saxon times this section of the Dorset coast was dominated by Wareham, one of Alfred's burhs, but by the middle of the century the trading ships were finding difficulties in entering Wareham harbour and commerce moved downstream to Poole. The town became a chartered port in 1248, and in the next century it became a favoured base for privateers. Of these, the most notorious was Harry Paye. In 1404, a fleet led by Paye and the Duke of Somerset was engaged by a combined French and Spanish fleet sailing from Harfleur. Paye's ship was captured and he was locked below with his crew to be sailed to France under escort. Then the Poole men broke their fetters and stormed through the hatches to reclaim their ship – and also took the French vessel which was acting as the escort. While even a Douglas Fairbanks Jnr might have considered this to be sufficient swashbuckling for one day, Paye and his crew then hoisted French colours, sailed up the Seine and harried the shipping there. For two or three centuries to follow, the line between piracy and patriotism was hard to define, if it existed at all. Often the privateers were left free to prey on foreign shipping because their contribution to English sea power was invaluable. However, there was always the risk that one of the great continental powers would be so provoked by English pirates that severe reprisals or attempts at invasion would result.

In the year following Paye's raid on the Seine, 'Arripay', as he was known to the French and Spanish, was sailing with Lord Berkeley when their ships encountered a French fleet off South Wales, which was engaged in supplying Owain Glyndwr's Welsh insurgents. Fifteen of the French ships were taken and burnt and the supply lines, which were vital to the sustenance of the rebellion, were thus broken. Later that year, however, a Spanish and French fleet launched a reprisal raid on Poole and the town and its shipping were severely damaged. But the next year Paye returned to the port in triumph, having captured 120 cargo ships. In the sixteenth century, Poole became involved in a more respectable if scarcely less dangerous trade, as its ships joined those of Dartmouth fishing for cod in the great fishery off Newfoundland, which John Cabot had discovered in 1497.

Both Yarmouth and Aberdeen also owed much of their prosperity to the fishing industry. In medieval times, the demand for fish was probably much greater than the supply. The Roman Catholic church held sway and prescribed that fish was the only form of protein which could be consumed on numerous days of the year, while fresh protein of all kinds was welcomed in the days before refrigeration. But there were also restrictions on the growth of fishing industries. Fish could be salted or dried but the primitive nature of the transport system made it difficult to distribute the catch in any form from the coastal fishing ports to the inland markets. During the Middle Ages, the lords of inland manors would often send a cart in the charge of a trusted villein to one of the little coastal towns to purchase salted herring for the assembled peasants to eat at their harvest feast.

In Saxon times, various fishing ports seem to have been established as seasonal settlements of huts which were occupied when shoals ran close to the coast and when there were lulls in the farming activities. In this way, Winterton in Norfolk may have been used as a winter base by the farmers of nearby East Somerton when they forsook the relative safety of the agricultural life to fish the shoals of codling as they passed the coast. In the course of the Middle Ages, some greater fishing ports, such as Grimsby and Lowestoft, developed, and yet much of the activity was carried out from little village anchorages which had few if any artificial harbour facilities. In some parts of Britain this situation survived until relatively recent times. In the late eighteenth century, dotted along the 250-km (150-mile) coast of north-east Scotland there were no less than seventy distinct fishing villages, with their combined population of about 9,000 people operating 300 small fishing boats.

The smaller medieval fishing settlements were not independent towns, but housed feudal communities controlled by the local manor. Perhaps the lords of these manors had a better awareness of the rewards of farming and market trading, for they seldom seem to have shown much initiative in the development of fishing industries. Alnmouth in Northumberland was something of an exception. Apparently an early-twelfth-century lord of Alnwick castle established the seaport at the mouth of the Aln to serve his stronghold, which lay just 8 km (5 miles) away. At the end of the Middle Ages, the harbour facilities were destroyed when the river changed its course and, in 1567, the local fishing industry was said to be decaying, although a third of the sixty households still living in Alnmouth were those of fishermen. A later survey in 1622 revealed that fishing was the only remaining activity, while now the village exists as a little tourist and retirement centre, its decline allowing its medieval street pattern to be preserved.

Cornwall is noted for its picturesque fishing villages, but they were relatively late arrivals on the medieval scene. Only Polperro, first mentioned in 1303, and Port Isaac, recorded in 1338, are known to have existed as villages before the Black Death in 1348, and the development of fishing may have represented an attempt to ward off the economic gloom which followed the plague. Mevagissey, one of the most picturesque of the Cornish ports, did not grow in a gradual and rambling way, but was deliberately created in the years around 1410. A triangular green was set out as the focus for the planned fishing village.

So long as Cornish fishermen were part-time farmers or were obliged to market as well as catch their fish, the industry was

*Nets drying on the shore
at Cove near Aberdeen*

bound to remain localised. By the close of the Middle Ages, fish merchants had appeared, while the skills gained in more glamorous building enterprises were being applied to the construction of the jetties which were needed to shield the exposed harbours. By Elizabethan times, Bude, Clovelly, Mousehole, Newlyn, Padstow and Newquay had joined the ranks of the Cornish fishing ports. In due course, fishing hamlets appeared at many now deserted coves.

For centuries, the Cornish fishermen relied upon traditional methods to catch a wide variety of fish. It was not until the start of the nineteenth century that a specialised industry arose, based on

using the seine-net method to catch pilchards for export to Roman Catholic countries, notably to Italy. The pilchard fishery had begun to be significant as early as the seventeenth century, but at first it was followed by part-timers, and to blossom it required the adoption of the new techniques and the improvements to docks and breakwaters which were undertaken at so many Cornish ports in Georgian and early-Victorian times. Huers, perched high on the cliffs, scoured the seas for the shoals of pilchard, and directed the vessels which bobbed on the waves below. A few huers' houses still survive, as on the cliffs near Newquay. On the ground floor of his cottage, the fisherman had his cellar, where he pressed, fumed and pickled his catch, while the bigger enterprises had vile-smelling 'fish palaces' or courtyards, where the work was carried out in the surrounding lean-to sheds. Some houses in parts of ports such as St Ives were built above such courtyards, but in the middle of the nineteenth century, the industry began gradually to decline.

In contrast to the Cornish seine-netters, the old fishermen of the ports of north-east Scotland used long lines to catch a different prey. As we have seen, the industry was dispersed amongst a multitude of little villages and hamlets, and fishermen here had only the most basic of equipment, while the harbours were often strewn with hazards. These Scots fished for 'great fish': cod, haddock, halibut, ling and skate. While the Poole and Dartmouth

Port Isaac, one of the oldest if less picturesque Cornish fishing villages

men were racing each year in seaworthy ships to gain the best toeholds on which to establish their processing plants on the Newfoundland shore, the fishermen from the coves of Aberdeenshire, Banffshire and Kincardineshire were operating in open boats, only around 7.5 m (25 feet) in length, at distances of 80 km (50 miles) or more from their homes. As with the Newfoundland fishery, the men took to the sea as early in the spring as the weather would allow. They fished with long lines, up to 3 kilometres (2 miles) in length and armed with as many as 2,000 hooks. Then, when the condition of the cod deteriorated as the year wore on, the Scots used lighter tackle to fish for haddock in waters closer to home. Being far from most large urban markets, the Scots could sell only a fraction of their catch as fresh fish, the remaining cod was salted, split and sun-dried and the haddock was smoked.

Life for the Scottish fishermen in the eighteenth century was fraught with peril, and almost every family will have had members who were lost at sea. But in return for braving the dangers of the sea, the families involved enjoyed a rare degree of independence on the land. Because the boats and equipment involved were relatively frail and simple, their costs were fairly modest. A boy would take to the sea in his early teens, and if he had survived to his twenties he would take a bride from within the little community and obtain a loan from his landowner-landlord which

would allow him to buy his own boat, as well as laying claim to a free plot of land on which to build his house. These cottages were built on cliff-foot shelves or on rocky perches, all with their gable walls turned towards the eastern gales. This arrangement also made it easier to pull up boats from the shore. The debt was repaid with a modest annual payment to the landlord-creditor, and so the fisherman enjoyed a degree of independence which was in striking contrast to the near-feudal conditions which survived in the neighbouring farming settlements.

While so many medieval fishermen had been part-time farmers, the fishing communities of north-east Scotland followed an existence which was quite distinct from that of all the folk living to landward. The fishing villages were closed communities; they did not accept incomers, and brides were found from within the seafaring society. Even today, fragments of this introspection survive in villages and hamlets where the most severe forms of Protestant worship are preserved, and where commonplace items from the modern world, like television and magazines, are regarded as inherently sinful.

As fishing was developing during the second half of the eighteenth century, the map of the countryside of north-east Scotland was being redrawn. The English victory at Culloden had left the Scottish landlords with no choice but to enter into the competitive world of British commerce. In the Highlands, the new economic reality produced the ghastly sheep clearances, but in the northern lowlands it gave birth to attempts to redeploy the surplus tenant farmers in local industries. Of these, fishing seemed to be one of the most promising. There were already plenty of old fishing settlements which had grown in a slow and piecemeal fashion. Some of these were redeveloped, while some new fishing villages were created on open ground. Cullen was an old village which straggled on a raised beach and on the cliff top above the 'seatoun', a new village with a neat geometrical plan was set out to house a community of displaced crofters. The old village of Ward of Cruden at Cruden Bay was redeveloped as Port Errol, and here a river was diverted to create an inlet where fishing craft could shelter. Gardenstown, still a bastion of religious introspection, was set out before the tidal wave of changes on a shelf at the foot of some towering red cliffs by the local worthy, Garden of Troup. To the north of the Moray Firth, Helmsdale was a new fishing village created by the Duke of Sutherland and Thurso and Lybster were developed by the agricultural reformer, Sir John Sinclair.

The fishing communities were deeply conservative, but they were also adaptable. This was shown at the end of the eighteenth century when herring began to be caught in large numbers off the coast of Caithness. The white fish line fishermen had to convert to the new craft of fishing with nets, but for the scores who did so it was possible to earn as much during the brief six-week-long summer herring season as it was during the whole year of fishing for cod and haddock. The little villages and hamlets grew rapidly in the century which followed, a few of them becoming five times as large as before. At the same time, the new-found prosperity began to undermine the old independence, for the costs of competitive fishing equipment increased enormously. Around 1840 a boat and a train of nets could be bought for about £50, but by 1880 the costs had risen to up to £400. Boat-owners now found themselves deeply in debt to the fish merchants who provided the loans. Family ownership still remained the norm, but soon the arrival of the much more costly steam drifters would strain the old independence still further, and people the villages with a new class of wage-earning fishermen. Meanwhile, the growth and modernisation of the industry concentrated the curing and marketing operations in fewer ports, places such as Aberdeen, Peterhead, Fraserburgh, Buckie and Banff. And yet, the fisherfolk remained a race apart, and if they lived in one of the larger towns then they established their own, closed little quarter within it, with the Aberdeen fishermen living around their harbour in the Torry and Footdee sections of the town.

While the fishing industry was flourishing along the eastern shores of Scotland and supporting a culture with its own very distinctive outlooks and lifestyle, the west coast was a sad and depressed area. Thousands of families which had been dislodged from the age-old clan territories by the clearances had gravitated to the seaboard, where they struggled to survive as crofters. Surely, it was thought, the development of a west-coast fishing industry could relieve the hardships and establish the foundations for prosperity? Unlike the folk of the east coast, however, the Highlanders had no great tradition of fishing. Here, fishing settlements such as Tobermory and Ullapool were sponsored by the British Fisheries Society, a semi-charitable organisation seeking to exploit the herring fishery. Mallaig, Oban and a few smaller ports enjoyed a measure of success, but the thrift, single-mindedness and the tightness of societies which had defined the east-coast communities and had served them so well could not be recreated. Even in the current century, when Lord Leverhulme pledged to make Stornoway on Lewis the greatest fishing port in Europe he found that his greatest adversaries were those who would have prospered most from his ambitious plans.

For me, it is interesting – but not always easy – to discover why a town or a village has a particular layout and why it came into being and then prospered or declined. But recreating atmosphere is another problem. There can be no doubt that centuries ago life on the coast had a spicy, electric quality which was less evident inland, and which scarcely survives today. For a start, the seaside places must have smelt differently. There was no fug of diesel fumes, and as the salty breezes swirled around the cottages they picked up the stench of fish from boats too long at sea and the acrid fumes from the curing sheds. Danger was everywhere. Few sailors could reasonably expect to die in old age or on land, and for every adult man there was the constant threat of the press gang. Any man walking the narrow, unlit alleys of a seaport at night risked being battered into unconsciousness to awaken at sea, bloody and with a status that had been arbitrarily transformed from that of a freeman to one scarcely better than that of a galley slave. His wife and family would neither be informed nor compensated. And then, of course, there were the smugglers. To enjoy credibility in the streets of the seaside today it seems that every pub, café and knick-knack shop must claim to have been a smugglers' den. Most of the claims are probably bogus, but the smugglers were real enough.

In the early days, they were known as 'owlers', for they signalled to their accomplices by imitating the call of the owl. In these medieval times, the emphasis was on smuggling wool out of the country to ports on the continent, and it was later that a vast industry developed to evade the taxes on a wide range of imported goods. The work of the owlers probably went back to the reign of Edward III, when a ban was placed upon the export of raw wool in order to encourage the growth of the domestic textiles industry. Smuggling was probably at its peak around the middle of the eighteenth century, when the black economy was so large that it may have employed some 20,000 full-time smugglers in Sussex and Kent alone. At this time, half or even three-quarters of the amounts consumed of some imported goods, including tea and spirits, arrived from smuggling rather than via lawful channels.

Smuggling tested the consciences of those people who had them. The smuggler could demand to know why he should show any consideration for a state or government which would quite cheerfully impress himself or any innocent family man into its navy. The customer could ask why the burden of taxation fell so heavily on goods such as salt, beer, tea and cocoa, which were almost basic essentials to the poorer classes, and why British people were expected to pay twice as much for their sugar as the French did. Meanwhile, the supporters of the official policies, few as they may have been, might have retorted that the government had to raise its revenue in some way, and the more that taxation was evaded by smuggling then the more it would have to be raised in other ways – so that the only people really to benefit were the smugglers themselves. But it was perfectly plain for all to see that smuggling could not have flourished without the active connivance of the majority of the public at large, and that, along the Channel coast in particular, smuggling was a major industry which connected thousands of people in its intricate and pervasive webs.

In the first quarter of the eighteenth century, the activities of the owlers, who were in close association with the sheep farmers of the Downs and the Romney Marsh, were beginning to decline, but the trade in illicit imports was growing. A contemporary account which captures the full flavour of coastal life was provided by Defoe: 'As I rode along this coast [Romney Marsh], I perceiv'd several dragoons, riding officers, and others arm'd and on horseback, riding always about as if they were huntsmen beating up their game; upon inquiry I found their diligence was employ'd in quest of the owlers, as they call them, and sometimes they catch some of them; but when I came to enquire farther, I found too, that often times these are attack'd in the night, with such numbers, that they dare not resist, or if they do, they are wounded and beaten and sometimes kill'd; and at other times are oblig'd, as it were, to stand still, and see the wool carry'd off before their faces, not daring to meddle; and the boats taking it in from the very horses' backs, go immediately off, and are on the coast of France, before any notice can be given of them, while the others are as nimble to return with their horses to their haunts and retreats, where they are not easily found out.'

Much smuggling involved secret networks as highly organised as those associated with the modern traffic in drugs, and the violence arising from the trade was no less. Smugglers were desperate men who would resort to almost any means to avoid capture. If caught with masks or blackened faces then they might be hanged, while otherwise they faced five years' service in the navy. Any boat which was thought to contain a larger crew than was necessary for lawful fishing or transport, or which was carrying sufficient sail to outrun a customs cutter was likely to be destroyed or confiscated. Yet the smuggler who was prepared to risk his boat or his freedom could expect handsome returns. Writing in 1892 about events sixty years earlier, a retired customs officer, H.N. Shore, described how a smuggler from a south-western port could buy 150 kegs of spirits at Roscoff in Brittany for £120. If he did not own a boat he could hire and crew one for £100, and when the consignment of brandy was safely smuggled into England it would be worth about £1,080. Distilleries catering specifically for the illicit English trade were established along the French coast, while the brandy, along with wine, lace, tea and tobacco were shipped across the Channel in fast boats, mainly at night and usually to the more remote beaches and quieter inlets. The boats employed were modified for speed, their bowsprits lengthened to carry great headsails, while it was illegal to own a rowing boat equipped with more than six oars. Often the smugglers would change or duplicate the names of their boats to confuse the excise men.

On some occasions, the balance of forces tipped quite markedly in favour of the smuggling fraternity. In Elizabethan times, the customs service was riddled with corruption, as would be expected in a situation where the officer purchased his office from the crown and then received very little by way of a salary. Even at the end of the seventeenth century, a Captain Southgate of the Preventive Service reported that: 'The vessels now in the smuggling trade become so large and formidable that we are not only repulsed, insulted and beat by them, but are actually in danger of being run down and sunk by them, who not only threaten to do so, but also attempted it.' Often the revenue men were outnumbered, and the arrogance and audacity of their adversaries could be remarkable. In 1813, the authorities impounded two tons of tea which had been run from Guernsey to Poole. It was locked in the old Customs House until the smuggler, John Diamond, arrived at the head of a gang of sixty men, broke into the house and took away almost the whole consignment. On this occasion the authorities were able to take effective action, and ten members of the gang were hanged.

Once ashore, the larger cargoes were met by teams of pack ponies and moved to a secure hiding place, as immortalised in Rudyard Kipling's 'Smugglers' Song':

> Five-and-twenty ponies
> Trotting through the dark –
> Brandy for the Parson,
> 'Baccy for the Clerk.
> Them that asks no questions isn't told a lie –
> Watch the wall, my darling, while the Gentlemen go by!

The safe havens and warehouses for the contraband were often inns, but in the real badlands of the trade the parish churches were often employed. In the Romney Marsh area the churches at Brookland, Fairfield, Ivychurch and Snargate were all involved in activities other than the salvation of souls. Whatever the arguments in its favour may have been, to some degree or other smuggling corrupted all those who were associated with it.

Honest revenue men were beaten and occasionally murdered, while others were bribed, blackmailed, and were, in some cases, smugglers themselves. The customers for the 'run goods' were sometimes intimidated, but generally were willing participants, so that only very rarely did they turn against the members of a particularly loathsome network – as happened to the notorious Hawkhurst gang in the eighteenth century, when the villagers of Goudhurst in the Weald formed a militia which drove the smugglers out of their village. But the more normal attitude of the public at large was demonstrated in 1821, when a suspect fishing boat skippered by one Joseph Swaine was searched by a Coast Blockade man. In a brawl which followed Swaine was shot and killed and the people of Hastings raised the grand sum of £99 for his widow by public subscription.

There is a large part of the British public which is ever-ready to support the most obnoxious causes so long as they can be dressed up in some sort of sentimental garb: those who keep fighting dogs are widely and rightly despised but there is a sizable minority which tolerate the dismemberment of live foxes by packs of dogs because the participants ride horses and wear red coats which they insist on calling pink. The same sort of muddle-headedness was shown by Charles Lamb when he wrote from Hastings: 'I like a smuggler. He is the only honest thief. He robs nothing but the revenue – an abstraction I never greatly cared about.' One wonders if he liked the Hastings smugglers who murdered three coastguards in a Martello tower in 1832, or who had severely injured two officers as they bravely attempted to prevent a run in the previous year. Such events were part and parcel of smuggling and were not uncommon. In 1813, for example, the Diamond gang intercepted a customs officer and his witness as they travelled to report to a magistrate, and both men were murdered.

It was probably the shortness of the Channel crossing that made the old Cinque Ports and the inlets of the Romney Marsh the centres of the smuggling trade, but most other sections of the English and Welsh coast were to some degree involved. The villagers of Cawsand, to the south of Plymouth, had a particular enthusiasm for smuggling, and at the start of the Victorian era, some fifty boats from the little harbour were thought to be engaged in illicit affairs. Deal was no sluggard in such matters, and its fishermen did not allow patriotic concerns to interfere with their traditional pursuits. During the Napoleonic wars, when the navy was preoccupied with fighting the French fleet, the smuggling of goods to and from blockaded France boomed. And after the wars, when the government was able to resume the campaign against smugglers, the Deal fishermen developed galleys or 'gigs' up to 24 m (80 feet) in length which could outrace most revenue cutters. As a result, the authorities were obliged to station three naval frigates to control the contraband traffic around the port.

Smuggling was never completely suppressed, and the reasons for its decline were various. It has been argued that the rise in tourism played an important part in stemming the illegal traffic. It was certainly true that tourism provided an attractive alternative income for the hard-pressed fisherman whose forbears had provided the backbone of the contraband industry. For a seaside tourist industry to come into being, there had to be a sizable class of people with time and money to spare, a change in fashions, and convenient ways of getting to the resorts. Tourism did not really exist in the Middle Ages, and the closest approach to holiday travel was pilgrimage. This was not confined to the wealthy classes, and was the only means by which most peasants or yeomen could expect to explore the wider world. The centres for pilgrimage were places associated with miracles and miracle cures and churches which held or had purchased holy relics, many of which were bogus. Of these various centres, a few happened to lie beside the coast. There is the wonderful St David's cathedral in old Pembrokeshire (now Dyfed), which got a great boost to its tourist trade early in the twelfth century, when Pope Callixtus II declared that two pilgrimages to St David's were equivalent to one to Rome itself. Nearby is the chapel of St Non, David's mother. Also on the Pembrokeshire coast is the tiny chapel of St Govan, wedged between two cliff bastions. Then there were the island holy places, St Michael's Mount in Cornwall, where storm-lashed fishermen had seen a vision of the Archangel, Bardsey Island, Lindisfarne, Iona and others.

After the Middle Ages, the fashion for the Grand Tour developed amongst the wealthy and cultivated classes. Classical culture was in fashion – and the continental countries had much more of it. Frontiers were more open, and French provided a lingua franca for educated people of all nationalities. The idea that one might spend a holiday in a British seaside setting would have seemed utterly bizarre, and it was developments in medical fashion rather than in recreation which provided the seeds from which the seaside holiday could germinate. In Germany and the Low Countries a fad for drinking the waters of sulphur or chalybeate

The coastal cathedral at St David's attracted many pilgrims

springs developed, apparently around the premise that the worse the cure tasted, then the more good it would do. Then English centres such as Bath, Harrogate, Buxton, Epsom and Wells began to emerge as spas. Scarborough was already a place of some historical importance. The Romans had a signal station on the cliffs nearby, and an important royal castle was built here in the reign of Henry II. Later, the town emerged as a trading and fishing port, and a quay was built quite early in the Middle Ages. In 1702, it was recorded that about 160 sail and collier ships lay in harbour here during the winter; the congestion being relieved by improvements to the harbour in the decades which followed. Scarborough also had mineral springs.

These medicinal springs were discovered on the sands in 1626, and this remarkable juxtaposition of sea and spa water set the seal on Scarborough's future. In 1660, a Dr Witte, a local physician, wrote a treatise on the wonderful properties of sea water. The springs lay in the poorer part of the town, around Newborough, and in the first years of the eighteenth century, coffee shops, taverns and booths were built here to exploit the growing tourist trade. The town began to rival the fashionable inland spas and, in 1705, it was said that 'most of the gentry of the North of England and Scotland resort hither in the season'. Scarborough could offer its guests the discomforts and alarming consequences of drinking both mineral water and sea water. The benefits were affirmed in 1702 by the London doctors, Floyer and Baynard, who itemised the various afflictions which sea water could cure and who suggested that there was yet more to be enjoyed:

> Cold bathing has this good alone
> It makes old John to hug old Joan.
> And does fresh kindness yet entail
> On wife tasteless, old and stale.

Scarborough was also probably the first place to advertise sea bathing; all for the good of their health, men and women were to be seen bathing naked here by the 1730s, though some took advantage of the bathing machines which disgorged their patrons at the water's edge, some modesty still intact.

Scarborough could not expect to retain its monopoly on this fad for very long, for it was plain that the sea at Scarborough could not be much different from the sea anywhere else. In 1750, a physician of Lewes, Richard Russell, published a work on the curative effects of sea water, and two years later he opened a clinic at Brighton. The south coast town had already attracted a few visitors, the first, according to local legend, being the Clarke family, who came in 1736.

Unlike Scarborough, Brighton had little obvious attraction as a resort, though before too long its reputation for sleaze with a certain measure of style was established. Contrary to popular myth, the town was not a decayed fishing village, although it did have distinct commercial disadvantages. As at Deal, there was no harbour and boats had to be hauled on to the shingle beach. By the beginning of the eighteenth century, this hazard was causing some trade to drift away, the decline being accelerated by storm damage to the beach in the years that followed – and which caused a hundred dwellings to be swept away. By 1724, when Defoe made his visit, the place was distinctly downcast and he found 'Bright Helmston' to be: 'a poor fishing town, old built and on the very edge of the sea. The sea is very unkind to this town,

*St Govan's chapel at
Bosherton on the
Pembrokeshire coast*

and has by its continual encroachments, so gained upon them, that in a little time more they might reasonably expect it would eat the whole town.' The people of Brighton were canvassing for a sum of £8,000 to rebuild their sea wall, though Defoe thought that this was more than the place was worth. Nonetheless, Brighton had supported some eighty deep sea fishing boats and four hundred fishermen in Elizabethan times, and when it exploited the herring fishing in the Stuart period it was the largest town in Sussex. Even at the dawn of its tourist industry it had around seventy fishing boats hauled up on the beach. Its landscape was flat and bare, with scarcely any visual charms, so these shortcomings were turned into an advantage by local physicians who warned against the poisonous vapours released by trees, the dilution of the brine by incoming rivers – and then trumpeted the superiority of waters that turned the bather blue with cold.

Local quacks began to restore Brighton's fortunes, but it was royal patronage which really put the town on the map again. As Nigel Calder explains, by 1780 Brighton had emerged as a health resort and was also becoming a fashionable centre for drinking and gambling: 'King George III then had two preoccupations: to keep George Washington out of New York and George, Prince of Wales, out of Brighton. In 1783 both his hopes were dashed.'*

* Nigel Calder, *The English Channel*, Chatto & Windus, 1986.

Brighton had many imitators. Shingle accumulating against breakwaters creates the zig-zag shoreline

Four years later, the prince began to convert the farmhouse which he had leased in order to be near his Mrs Fitzherbert into the Royal Pavilion, the work continuing on and off beyond the coronation and until 1822. Byron echoed the popular sentiments when he wrote:

> Shut up the King – No the Pavilion
> Lest it will cost us all another million!

It was during the Pavilion-building period that Brighton became the European centre for fashionable debauchery, a place where every rake and buck could have his fling. One contemporary critic savaged not only the immodest design of the bathing machines, which apparently lacked discreet awnings, but also the morals of those armed with telescopes, the better to observe the contents of these machines as they prepared and then emerged to sprawl and flounder.

The people of other run-down places along the coast studied

events at Brighton with interest. As Weymouth emerged as a resort it followed a more righteous course: here a gap of 50 m (about 50 yards) parted the bathing machines used by the different sexes. Radipole, close by, had been a port in Roman times, and in the fourteenth century, Weymouth had become a sufficient nuisance to the French to merit a raid on its harbour in 1377. In Elizabethan times, it merged with Melcombe Regis, just to the north, and the twin town sent six ships to fight the Armada. In the middle of the eighteenth century, Weymouth began to establish itself as a resort and, in 1789, all its dreams were answered when it received a visit from George III and his queen. How can we recapture the splendour and pageantry of the occasion when, as the regal torso was engulfed by a wave, a band, furtively secreted in an adjacent bathing machine, gave forth the national anthem? The king came back for more, sometimes guarded by a naval squadron; none could deny the wisdom of such precautions, for were the king to be snatched by a French raiding party at the very moment of his ablutions, the Prince Regent was next in line.

Tourism revitalised the economies of some declining towns, and it also gave birth to new centres. Bournemouth was another place which sought to be rather less naughty than Brighton. At the beginning of the nineteenth century, there was nothing there but a desolate heath, but when the barren sands were planted with pines, the beaches below became irresistible to the developers. In 1830, Bournemouth had just a few cottages, and during the four decades which followed, its growth was staid and genteel. Then the railway arrived, and during the next two decades the town quadrupled in size. It has been growing ever since.

The railways played a vital part in devising the map of British resorts, and they allowed new social classes to visit the seaside. Scarborough, Brighton and Weymouth were upper-class resorts which emerged at a time when only the upper classes were able to take the cure and enjoy the associated frolics. In the middle decades of the nineteenth century, resorts frequented by the middle classes expanded at places like Broadstairs, New Brighton, Walton-on-the-Naze and Weston-super-Mare. But the great mass of the working population was still bound to hearth and home at holiday time. The railways put an end to this. Saltburn is the Victorian creation of the entrepreneur, Henry Pease. The world's first railway ran from Stockton to Darlington, and this railway was extended to Saltburn to provide the people of the Teeside industrial towns with their own place in the sun. The railway terminated at a railway hotel and a Saltburn Improvement Company was established to encourage developers to add to the line of tall hotels and boarding houses growing along Marine Parade. The later growth was more modest, so that the Victorian seaside town character still endures.

This sort of character had become established by the 1860s. In 1865, Lewis Carroll described how 'Alice' had come to the conclusion that 'wherever you go on the English coast you find a number of bathing machines in the sea, some children digging in the sand with wooden spades, then a row of lodging houses, and behind them the railway station.' This was the mantle adopted by New Hunstanton in Norfolk. It was built on a green-field site where the coloured cliffs, banded in a geological layer cake, met the salt-marshes, and it was 2 km (about a mile) from the old Hunstanton village. During the first half of the century, its growth was slow, but in the 1860s, New Hunstanton enjoyed the patronage of the local landowner, Hamon le Strange, and began to spread. It was composed of tall, mock-Tudor houses built in rows according to the dictates of a grid pattern of streets which sprang from the margins of a large, triangular green running up to the edge of the cliffs. The railway from the south arrived in 1862, and then the resort gained a church, a 250-m (800-foot) pier, a union church to be shared by all nonconformists, hotels, a country club, a theatre and a golf course. It became the epitome of the seaside resort – but then so, too, did a great many other places.

The railway played a major part in launching a series of new resorts established along a 64-km-long (40-mile-long) zone of the North Welsh coast. Inland, the scenery was splendid, but this was not what was being marketed. The coast, however, faced the wrong way, the beaches having their fronts to the cool winds and their backs to the sun. But all this was offset by the fact that the coast lay within handy reach of the swelling industrial centres of Liverpool, Manchester and the North Midlands. Development on a grand scale was made possible by Stephenson's choice of a coast-hugging route for the railway bound from Chester for the Irish Sea packet station which was expanding at Holyhead. Llandudno, Colwyn Bay and Rhyl were three of the most important resorts which emerged, and though they had much in common they also had important differences.

Llandudno has a magnificent site on a peninsula between two bays, and with the main beach bracketed by the bulging limestone headlands of the Great Orme and Little Orme. It is said to have

The sea front at Bournemouth

owed its genesis to a chance remark made by a Liverpool surveyor at a meeting of local copper-mine shareholders, when he commented on the splendour of the sandy beaches and landscape. The agent for the Mostyn family, who owned the surrounding land, passed on the comments, and the family then obtained an Enclosure Award to establish their title to the area. In 1848, the Mostyns auctioned most of the land to developers, but they included a number of restrictions in the contracts – and these covenants are still strongly reflected in the character of the resort. Llandudno took shape as a rigidly planned town with a grid pattern of streets, and with districts in which only large houses with wide frontages were accepted. The urban landscape was spacious; the main departure from geometrical planning was found on The Crescent, where hotels and genteel residences followed the sweep of the Llandudno Bay. The commerce of the young resort was given a kick start by the arrival of the railway in 1858, not the main line but a branch, and as the resort grew it remained fairly true to the original concept of a superior, stylish and floral place of a sedate rather than a raucous character.

While Llandudno was emerging in a closely controlled eruption, Colwyn Bay, just to the east, was developing in a more leisurely and aimless manner. The railway arrived at the midpoint of the century, but at first it only stimulated a scatter of growth around the station. Every resort clamoured for its railway, but in this woeful case the track was built atop a massive embankment which formed a barrier between the town and its beach. The land here was owned by the Erskine family, but in 1865 their estate was auctioned. Half was bought by one John Pender and the other half was sold in small lots. Ten years later, Pender sold to a development syndicate, and this land was developed with parallel, tree-lined avenues running between elegant three-storey brick residences. Meanwhile, to the north of the coastal road and around the railway station, the resort had developed in a much more cramped and haphazard pattern, while slotted between the railway and the sea there was The Parade, which ran westwards to a great Victorian hotel. In 1900 Colwyn Bay gained that essential symbol of Victorian resort virility: a pier.

Rhyl, the largest of the resorts of the North Wales coast, demonstrated that it was possible to become a holiday centre without waiting for the railway, and that planned esplanades and disciplined avenues were not prerequisites for the attraction of visitors. Situated on the sandy warrens and marshland of an old common close to Edward I's castle town of Rhuddlan, the locality gained hot and cold baths in 1835 and set about exploiting the fashion for sea bathing, so that by the middle of the century there was a substantial village of shops, inns and hotels. It was in the second half of the century, after the coming of the railway, however, that the town experienced explosive growth. Long terraces running down to the shore were built in the strip of land, almost 2 kilometres (a mile) in width, which lay between the railway and the sea. The development was neither spacious nor coherent, but in 1867 local enterprise furnished the first pier to split the sea along the northern coast of Wales. Land around Clwyd that was too prone to floods for building became a lake and pleasure park,

while warrens were levelled to form summer gardens. More recently, estates of retirement bungalows have spread into the surrounding marshland – but Rhyl did not set out to be a place of gentle refinement and it remains a symbol of full-blooded Victorian entrepreneurship.*

Few resorts can boast a natural setting to equal that of Llandudno

* The material on the resorts of North Wales is condensed from *Landscapes of North Wales*, Roy Millward and Adrian Robinson, David and Charles, 1978.

189

On the coast of North Wales the holiday industry spawned and nurtured towns in settings which had been desolate. In Cornwall its impact has been rather different; it has engulfed local communities and done much to destroy that which it sought to extol. In its unspoilt days, the attractions of the Duchy were obvious and immense, though Cornwall suffered because of its distance from London and other great centres of population. The climate and sea are warmer than elsewhere in Britain, and the blockade on foreign travel imposed by the Napoleonic wars encouraged the existing small-scale traffic in visitors and bathers.

But access was the key to success, and the door to Cornwall was unlocked in 1859, when the opening of the Ashness Bridge gave the local railways their link with the world beyond. The centres which welcomed the first tidal waves of visitors were those grafted to the network, such as Bude, Falmouth, Looe, Newquay, Padstow and Penzance. Pretty little places apparently doomed by the decline of the pilchard industry suddenly received an unexpected reprieve. Then, in the present century, the arrival of the motor car and the coach tour allowed the tourist industry to extend its tentacles towards the cliff-perched villages which the railway had scorned, and they too were revitalised and transformed. Cornwall and Blackpool receive very roughly the same numbers of visitors each year. At the 'tabloid' resort a relatively short and not-too-beautiful stretch of the Lancashire coast has been turned into something brazen, gaudy and now, some might say, rather jaded. Little of great value was destroyed and Lancashire was scarcely diminished after hatching its raucous chick. In Cornwall, however, visitors from rather different backgrounds have transformed a great landscape, a culture, perhaps even a nation. Cornwall has been loved to death, its reality swamped by parody and exploitation. In the search for salvation its soul was lost.

In the tourist industry it seems that even the best of intentions can embody the seeds of destruction. Perhaps Clovelly, just over the Cornish border in Devon, provides the proof of this. The village is a creation of patronage. Around 1370, the hamlet became a possession of the Cary family, and in late Tudor times, Sir George Cary sponsored its growth into a fishing village which was able to boast the only secure anchorage on the hazardous coast between the Taw estuary and the cliffs of North Cornwall. At a time when other south-western fishing ports were also growing, Clovelly was endowed with warehouses, salting cellars and a jetty. The village as it existed through into Victorian times was home to farmers and fishermen. The living was hard and families faced death every time the boats took to sea. Early in the eighteenth century the community was severely diminished; two storms, one in 1821 and another seventeen years later, between them drowned fifty-three men from the Clovelly fishing fleet. Then, very gradually, the village discovered that its face might be its fortune. Dickens wrote about it, Charles Kingsley was the son of the village Rector, and Turner and Whistler painted the place.

Always the subject of patronage and unified control, Clovelly was never going to fall victim to chaotic commercialism. The Hamlyns had bought the village from the Cary family in 1738 and, in 1884, Christine Hamlyn inherited the estate. For more than fifty years she exerted a firm control, repairing, titivating, rebuilding, providing new facilities for the residents and keeping at bay the tacky and garish clutter of the tourist industry which was already beginning to deface other West Country resorts. Yet she could not keep the visitors at bay, and the prettier Clovelly became, then the more people wanted to see it. And so, despite the fact that the village landscape is – give or take the odd Visitor Centre – as quaint and tasteful as can be, the lasting image retained by the discerning visitor is not one of cottages and cobbled slopes but of other visitors. Visitors with cameras, with ice creams, with dogs, in shorts, in sandals, in sweat shirts and jabbering away in the dialects of Bayswater and Birmingham, Braintree and Bristol. They are there like wanderers on a beach who admire the glorious shell of an organism which died long ago. Tourism provided the answer to many a failure, but nobody has found an answer to its success.

Chapter Nine

FROM LONDON TO LAND'S END

The coast of southern England has a remarkable diversity of scenery. It displays virtually every kind of coastal feature except a sea loch. There are drowned valleys and fast-growing shingle beaches, old ports left high, dry and destitute and, in the west, towering cliffs of ancient rock which seem to defy the power of the waves, while low salt-marshes and white walls of chalk are found in the east.

Where better to begin this perambulation of the coastline of mainland Britain than at **Swanscombe** by the south bank of the Thames estuary? It was here, in 1935, in the gravels of a high river terrace, that a dentist and fossil hunter, A.T. Marston, discovered the first fragment of the skull of a woman who had lived in southern England around 200,000 years ago. At this time, the climate was temperate but rather cool, the riverside setting was open and grassy but hemmed by woods of birch, alder and pine, and rhinos, cave lions and straight-tusked elephants roamed the plain. Now, with traffic erupting from the maw of the Dartford tunnel, it would be hard to imagine a scene less evocative of the Eden inhabited by the Swanscombe woman.

This is old dockland. At the start of the nineteenth century, London's docks spread eastwards down the estuary as far as Tilbury on the north bank of the river. Within little more than a hundred years, almost 80 km (50 miles) of quays were built, but in the last third of the present century, a rapid decline began. London's traffic congestion and the new fashion for massive freighters and containerisation lured the commerce to places such as Harwich and Rotterdam, with their modern facilities and different labour relationships. The southern shores of the Thames estuary have been transformed by the drainage of coastal marshes and the building of new embankments, which have reclaimed sheep grazings and narrowed the river. But Nature has not been evicted completely from the doorstep of the capital. From the Eastcourt Meadows country park by the Medway estuary there are views across a landscape of marshes, creeks and islands, while at the RSPB reserve of Elmley Marshes in the south of the Isle of Sheppey the fringes of the old salt-marshes are a breeding ground for duck, including pochard, shelduck, shoveler and tufted duck, as well as a variety of waders. Yet in settings such as these the threats to wildlife abound and multiply; the oyster industry of the north Kent coast was just beginning to recover from pollution damage when the stocks were blighted by the effects of TBT anti-fouling paint.

Previous page:
Harbour installations at
the foot of the chalk cliffs
at Dover

The eastern limits of the Thames estuary are marked by the crumbling cliffs at **Reculver**. This was the site of the Roman shore fort of Regulbium, which guarded the northern end of the strait which then separated the Isle of Thanet from the mainland. Erosion has eaten away the soft cliffs, and the northern section of the fort has been lost. Breakwaters help to reserve the magnificent remains of the great monastic church of St Mary, which was built inside the Roman defences and where the spectacular twin towers now stand close to the edge of the cliff. Just along the coast at **Birchington** the chalk cliffs are also eroding, but here the sea has created a picturesque fretwork of little inlets and headlands.

Near the thumb on the Kentish fist is **Margate**, one of the first seaside places to stake a claim in the tourist trade. There was sea-bathing here in the eighteenth century, and in Georgian times, great numbers of visitors would arrive from the capital in little boats. As the Thanet resorts developed, each one acquired its own personality. Margate became a brash, go-getting sort of place, competing with Southend for its share of the London trade; Broadstairs adopted a gentler and more genteel approach, while **Ramsgate** became a family resort and has found it difficult to come to terms with the decline of the traditional week-at-the-seaside type of holiday. Perhaps Ramsgate enjoyed its heyday during the Middle Ages, when it was a subsidiary port of Sandwich, or perhaps it enjoyed it before car ownership made families footloose at holiday times. But the town's greatest moment came in the December of 1748. Beset by storms, the ships in the Channel took refuge in the sheltered waters of the Downs, between the Kentish coast and the Goodwin Sands. On this occasion, however, the storms proved too severe, and one by one the vessels made a run for the rather primitive harbour at Ramsgate – and there they survived the tempest, though the harbour was almost choked with ships.

Ramsgate remains a port, but the seafaring days of **Sandwich** are long gone. Nearby, the Romans had their shore fort of Rutupiae or Richborough to guard the southern entrance to the Wantsum Channel, and just as Richborough was the Roman port of arrival to Britain, so Sandwich was favoured by England's medieval kings on their voyages to and from the continent. Across the channel from Sandwich was the Saxon port of Stonar, which remained quite important until the sea washed across it in 1365 and the French burned what remained two decades later. Sandwich was also a Saxon port and at the end of that era it had

gained a royal palace and a naval base. In 1226 it won independence of monastic control by Christchurch, and was an important
Cinque Port. Since 1457, its mayors have worn black, in mourning
for the events in 1457 when a French force, 4,000 strong, pillaged
the town. But more permanent destruction was in store, and in
the century which followed, the townsfolk waged a losing battle
against the silting of their harbour. It was still possible for a mock
naval battle to be staged in the harbour when Queen Elizabeth I
visited the town in 1573, as part of a concerted campaign to obtain
royal assistance in the campaign against the retreat of the sea. In
the middle of the next century, the port still had three dozen ships
even though it was becoming ever more difficult to use the harbour. Nothing more could be done. Although a community of
Flemish weavers was attracted to establish a cloth industry, fate
decreed that Sandwich would not be renowned as a great trading
port but remembered for the Earl of Sandwich who, in the 1760s,
demanded slices of beef served between pieces of toast so that he
could eat without diverting from the gaming tables – thus giving
birth to the snack which bears the town's name.

Next we come to a heavily fortified section of the invasion coast.
The Downs – not the chalk ridges but the stretch of water between
the Goodwin Sands and the Kentish shore – has been a great
thoroughfare and haven for shipping and a place where ships
would gather as they waited for the westerlies to drop to allow
passage westwards. At **Deal**, in sailing days, there was a community of 'hovellers', who at times when storms in the Downs caused
the sheltering ships to drag their anchors would take to sea in
small boats which carried enormous anchors. Rowing and sailing
through the heaving waves, the hovellers would, for a fee, bend a
cable from a stricken vessel to their great anchor and save the ship
from drifting and foundering. In a great storm of 1703, the long-
shoremen of Deal saved 200 lives on a day when 360 ships were
lost and 1,500 seamen were drowned. During the reign of Henry
III, three great castles were built to guard this busy, dangerous
and vulnerable section of coast against invasion. Sandown Castle
fell a victim to the sea, but Deal Castle remains extremely impressive with its stacked artillery platforms giving a command of the
sea and countryside for more than 2 km (a mile) around. Walmer
Castle has much less of a military bearing, and exists as the official
residence of the Lords Warden of the Cinque Ports; several distinguished politicians and soldiers were awarded this office when
late in life, and the Duke of Wellington died when in residence at

Walmer Castle. Somewhere between Deal and Walmer is thought to be the place where Julius Caesar landed for his reconnaissance in force into Celtic Britain – though the actual landing place now lies well out beneath the sea.

In prehistoric times, the harbour at **Dover** must have been provided by the mouth of the River Dour, though much later the river was culverted and the market place was built over the site of the natural harbour. A great hillfort, destined a thousand years later to accommodate the Norman castle, overlooked the harbour, while during the Roman occupation, Dover and Richborough were the principal Channel ports. Dover had the most important Roman naval base, and this was converted into a fort of the Saxon shore in the third century. Unlike so many of its neighbours, Dover has managed to maintain its importance despite the threat posed by the eastward drift of harbour-choking sand. During the Middle Ages, with the outlet of the Dour silted up, Dover, like Deal, became an open beach port. At the end of the fifteenth century, a pier was built to shield the first artificial harbour, but this haven soon fell victim to the eastward drift of the shingle – and the more that the breakwater was lengthened, the more the shifting pebbles curved around its tip. So the town once more became a beach port. A century after the creation of the first harbour, a new attempt was made. Inner and outer harbours were built; water was impounded in the inner work at high tide and then released to flush out the sediments from the outer harbour when the tide retreated.

This only provided a brief respite from the distinct natural disadvantages of the setting. The port managed to cling to a thread of life, though when Charles II landed here at the Restoration, the town was decaying, and at the beginning of the eighteenth century it sustained a mere seven ships. But the defensive significance of the site dominated by the great medieval castle was never overlooked. New military works on the Western Heights were begun in 1793, continued through the Napoleonic era, and were revitalised in the mid-nineteenth century. With heavily defended bunkers, dug-outs and barracks in the cliff and at the castle, it was planned that, in the event of a successful French landing, the enormous Dover garrison could emerge from its hidey-holes to attack the enemy supply lines. It was only after the first third of the nineteenth century that the expertise and resources necessary to salvage this convenient but stricken port were available. The Wellington Dock was built over the late-

Fine chalk cliff scenery at St Margaret's at Cliffe, in Kent

sixteenth-century harbour, and a floating dock and pier were added. In the last decade of the century, this pier was lengthened and a new one begun. By 1909, the works were complete and Dover was reborn as one of the safest and most extensive anchorages on the shores of Britain, and it remains by far the most important of the passenger ports. How its status will be affected by the completion of the Channel Tunnel remains to be seen.

The chalk forms fine cliffs between Deal and Dover, and to the west of Dover steep cliffs and landslips are seen at The Warren near **Folkestone**, while to the west of the harbour 'The Leas' are cliffs cut in Greensand. Folkestone was a modest port in medieval times, and declined in the centuries which followed, after the sea had eaten into its harbour. It found its salvation in the railway, which came in 1853, and provided not only swarms of holidaymakers but also the sponsorship for a new harbour. Since the 1970s, the port has also flourished as a passenger ferry terminal.

Just along the coast is **Hythe**, originally the little out-port of Saltwood, but a place which grew to become one of the original Cinque Ports (from the French *cinq*). Along with its four fellow members – Hastings, New Romney, Dover and Sandwich – Hythe was granted special privileges in the early eleventh century; later the 'five' was increased to seven with the addition of Rye and Winchester. These all eventually became 'head ports' and had thirty other satellite ports in Kent and Essex. In the course of the Middle Ages, shingle gradually choked Hythe's lifeline to the sea. Previously, it had been a trading port so large and prosperous that it had four churches, while the Hythe fishermen competed with their rivals at Great Yarmouth in the valuable herring fishery. The town was raided by the continental powers, and its continuing significance to the defence of the realm was marked at the beginning of the nineteenth century by the cutting of the Royal Military Canal, which ran for 50 kilometres (30 miles) from the Kent port to Rye in Sussex, and which was fortified by artillery to provide a defensible border detaching a highly vulnerable section of coast. Just inland from Hythe is Lympne, a vital Roman port and shore fort, although its harbour had become choked with shingle by Norman times.

At the dawn of history, the **Romney Marsh** existed as an expanse of tidal marshes which filled a bay cut by the sea in the soft Wealden clay. The formation of the Marsh was influenced by the accumulation of successive shingle ridges, known locally as 'fulls', each one marking a former shoreline. At one time a great ridge seems to have run through Lydd and New Romney in a north-east to south-west direction, straight across the mouth of the bay containing Romney Marsh, but subsequent ridges became ever more angular, jutting seawards to form the promontory of Dungeness. Waves driven by the prevailing south-westerlies, and at other times by the north-easterlies, seem to have rolled shingle along the seabed to give Dungeness its outline. Between Saxon times and the end of the Middle Ages, all the marsh to the south of the 'Rhee Wall', which follows the track from Romney to Appledore, had been reclaimed and much to the north of the wall as well. During the Napoleonic wars, the wall at Dymchurch was strengthened, guarding the coast in an area starved of shingle by the great accumulation of flinty pebbles at Dungeness to the south.

In Roman times, Old Romney and Lydd may have existed as island settlements on the dunes and shingle banks which protected the marsh. It is thought that the River Rother formerly flowed across the marsh and had its mouth at Romney, allowing the town to flourish as an estuarine port, until a great sea storm in 1287 diverted the river and caused it to enter the sea past the walls of Rye. The storm is commemorated by a great shingle ridge which is more than 1 km (about a mile) from the present shoreline and which stands more than 9 m (30 feet) above the current high watermark. New Romney is really quite old, a town planned in Saxon times on a grid with four long streets linked by various short cross streets. It became a Cinque Port, though Old Romney, nearby, was probably silted up by the time of the Norman conquest. Long regarded as a Roman sea wall, the Rhee Wall has been reinterpreted as a mid-thirteenth-century canal cut by the folk of New Romney in an attempt to keep the Rother flowing into their anchorage. The nuclear power stations at Dungeness are built in a place with earthquake-prone faults where shingle is dug and shifted by squads of lorries to preserve the shoreline – a fitting testimony to the wisdom of those who imposed such an industry on the nation.

In Saxon times, **Rye** existed as a little harbour on an island, and it might possibly have existed earlier as a Roman port for the export of iron from the Weald. This trade certainly existed in medieval times, when Rye had become a subsidiary of the Cinque Port of Hastings. Then, in 1287, the town benefited greatly – at the expense of its neighbour in the marsh – by acquiring the outlet of the Rother. In recognition of Rye's contribution to naval activities in the Channel, the town was wholeheartedly burned and pillaged by the French in 1377. This was the third major raid on the town to take place in that century, and there was another in 1448. By the end of the Middle Ages, however, the place had become too reduced to be of much trouble to anyone. The shingle, ever creeping eastwards, was clogging the mouth of the Rother and pushing back the sea, and trade was drifting away from the failing Cinque Ports to the western harbours. The narrow, shallow channel could still be used by a few fishermen and was of great interest to smugglers, but the fate of Rye seemed to be sealed. And yet the town refused to die, and in the nineteenth century, Rye-based schooners brought a small revival of its fortunes. It did not crumble, and endures as a tourist haven and one of the prettiest of the old towns on the south coast. Winchelsea did crumble and its

Not so very long ago smugglers would have plotted in alleys and the carriageways off inns, like this one at Rye

medieval successor became fossilised, as we have seen. High, dry and all alone on the reclaimed land between the neighbouring Cinque Ports stands the shell of the Henrician fort, Camber Castle.

Few stretches of open cliff countryside survive along this popular and congested coastline, but there is a passage of wilder scenery at Fairlight Glen, where a juxtaposition of sandstone and clay creates gorse-clad cliff faces scarred by landslips. **Hastings** developed in Saxon times with its face to the sea and its back shielded by the Pevensey Levels and the Romney Marsh. It was the most westerly of the Cinque Ports and shared in their saga of

hard times, losing its harbour in the course of the Middle Ages, and becoming a mere beach port. Near-fatal burnings by French raiding parties took place in 1339 and 1377. The town showed the same tenacity as was shown by Rye, and the post-medieval centuries were punctuated by ill-fated attempts to build a new harbour. Quite sizable ships were built on and launched from the beaches here, while colliers and other trading vessels were run on the beach at high tide, hurriedly unloaded, and floated off at the next high tide. St Leonards, on the western outskirts of Hastings, is a purpose-built resort, created for visitors of quality in Georgian times by the London builder, James Burton.

Gorse-clad cliffs of sand and clay at Fairlight

Between Hastings and Eastbourne are the old salt-marshes of the Pevensey Levels, with the stranded yet fascinating remains of Pevensey Castle. After landing hereabouts William the Conqueror took shelter in the ruins of a Roman shore fort as he began to consolidate his invasion. Originally, swamps had guarded the landward approaches to the fort and the waters of a harbour lapped its walls. The Normans patched up the Roman walls, which then became the defences of the outer bailey. A keep was built and, in the thirteenth century, an inner bailey with semi-circular towers was added. In the course of the Middle Ages, a shingle promontory developed to protect the Levels, but rather than growing further, it was gradually reduced, and now survives as a series of shingle ridges which culminate at Langley Point.

The scenery of the Channel coastline achieves its greatest glory at **Beachy Head**, where the cliffs of pure white chalk tower to a height of 163 m (536 feet) and seem completely defiant, despite the fact that they are retreating from the onslaught of the waves at an average rate of about 1 m (3 feet) each year. Sheltered from the westerlies by this headland of the Downs lies **Eastbourne**, less pickled in history than its eastern neighbours and developed during the nineteenth century under the patronage of the Dukes of Devonshire. It was here, in 1905, that Claude Debussy composed *La Mer*; there could scarcely be a better tribute to the pleasures of the seaside. The pageant of splendid chalk cliff scenery continues at Birling Gap and the Seven Sisters. Seaford has an Iron Age hillfort nearby and stands upon a Roman burial ground. It was an outlier of the Cinque Port of Hastings, with a harbour formed by the mouth of the River Ouse. During a storm in 1578, however, the river changed its course and entered the sea at Meething which, not surprisingly, became known as Newhaven.

In the south-coast world of stockbrokers' retreats and mega-mortgages the cliff-top bungalow settlement of **Peacehaven** is more refreshing than pretty. It was built after the Great War by former soldiers, who used their meagre gratuities to purchase toeholds in tranquillity following the horrors they had endured on the battlefields. We have already been to **Brighton** (see p. 182) and next comes **Shoreham** at the mouth of the Adur. Somewhere on the river mouth there was a Roman port, while Old Shoreham was a Saxon settlement and an important medieval naval and priva-teering port. It sent some twenty-six ships to the siege of Calais in 1346. During the Middle Ages, sailing ships could pass upstream and tie up under the walls of Bramber Castle, but gradually the drifting shingle diverted the outlet of the river eastwards; during the nineteenth and present centuries, the making of cuts, locks and piers has kept the harbour open.

Worthing, with its shingle beach compartmentalised by break-waters, is a family holiday resort in the traditional manner. Formerly a fishing hamlet, it grew under the patronage of Princess Amelia at the same time that her brother, the Prince Regent, was having his way with Brighton. **Bognor** is another purpose-built resort, created in the late eighteenth century by Sir Richard Hotham as one more attempt to emulate the success of Brighton. But Queen Victoria liked it, and after George V had recuperated here it became Bognor Regis. **Selsey Bill** marks the western end of the bay on this active coastline. Selsey was once an island; there was a Roman port here and later a Saxon cathedral city which was destroyed by the sea, causing the bishop to move the see to Chichester in 1075, where the new cathedral was completed in 1108. Chichester was a port on a creek in Saxon times and one of the ten leading ports by the fourteenth century. But by the seventeenth century, merchant ships of any size were unable to reach the harbour, and its trade passed to Emsworth.

Long ago, even the **Isle of Wight** was not an island and the area occupied by the harbours at Portsmouth, Langstone and Chichester was low-lying ground drained by streams which flowed southwards. A chalk ridge running from the Isle of Purbeck to the Isle of Wight caused the Frome to flow along its north side in a valley now inundated to form the Solent and Spithead. When this ridge was breached by sea and river erosion the soft rocks of the old Frome valley were soon worn away and the Isle of Wight came into being. Much later, the excellence of the area as a base for naval operations was exploited. A sailing fleet moored in **Spithead** could take to sea despite the direction of the wind, yet Portsmouth harbour, nearby, provided a sheltered and easily defended haven for fleets which were ideally placed to emerge and exert their control over the waters of the Channel. The Romans had their naval base close by the harbour mouth at Portchester. The docks at **Portsmouth** were walled in 1213, but the town experienced four severe French raids during the century which followed. Further defences were built at the harbour mouth, and in Tudor times the town emerged as a formidable naval base. England's first naval dry dock was built here in 1495. After centuries of greatness, Portsmouth has surrendered its naval supremacy to Plymouth, but Henry VIII's *Mary Rose*, Nelson's *Victory* and Victoria's *Warrior* are preserved here.

During the Civil War, Portsmouth was a royalist bastion, while **Southampton** favoured Parliament. As a result, Southampton was starved of royal patronage for a while after the Restoration, but this was but one small chapter in a long story of fluctuating fortunes. The town served as a port of embarkation for the Plantagenet possessions in France, and when these territories were lost, it preserved a naval function. Then strong trade links with the Mediterranean were developed, and Southampton was visited by Venetian merchants from 1378 until the end of the Middle Ages. But by this time, the town's commerce was suffering in competition with ports to the west and east. By Georgian times, the commercial future seemed quite bleak, and Southampton's best prospects appeared to lie in adopting a role as yet another Brighton clone. The Napoleonic wars helped to revitalise the port, but they did not last long enough so far as Southampton was concerned. The railway to London was begun in 1838, and in 1842 the P&O steamers began to use the port. The bigger the liners became, the better it was for Southampton as, for complex reasons relating to the town's midway position on the Channel, the port was able to boast 'double high water' or four high tides a day, which allowed deep-drafted liners to navigate a course around the offshore sandbanks without undue delay. This passenger traffic grew and grew during the present century, until the start of the 1960s, when the liners were handling an average of around a thousand passengers per day – and then air travel very swiftly captured almost all the traffic.

From Southampton Water we move westwards along the Solent to picturesque **Lymington**, once noted as a centre of the salt-making industry. Brine evaporated in a series of pans or lagoons, and the process was completed in iron pans which were heated by coal. Coastal saltings must have existed in prehistoric times and others were established on the East Anglian coast by the Romans. The saltways which led to the inland markets are amongst the oldest of our roads and trackways. Eventually, the pumping of brine from deposits on land concentrated the industry in Cheshire, important as a focus of saltways for many centuries. **Hengistbury Head**, to the west of Christchurch Bay, was defended by double banks and existed as one of the earliest of our international ports. In the late Iron Age, seamen of the Coriosolite tribe living in Brittany would sail from their port of Alet with cargoes of amphorae of wine from Bordeaux and Italy. They would either make the 250-km (150-mile) crossing direct or, if conditions were unfavourable, they would rest at Guernsey until the winds moved into the right quarter. At Hengistbury the cargoes were unloaded and replaced by British metalware, agricultural products and, quite possibly, slaves.

As we have seen, **Bournemouth** erupted from the coastal heathlands during the nineteenth century (see p. 185), though **Poole**, on its margins, has a long and colourful history. Its fortunes were founded on its fine natural harbour, one of the drowned valleys which abound along the shores of Hampshire and Dorset. As the submerged floor of the valley silted, so trade gravitated from the old Saxon burh of Wareham to Poole in the mid-twelfth century. Before too long the port was renowned and feared as a base of pirates and privateers. In 1497 John Cabot sailed into Poole after his 'discovery' of Newfoundland. He had been beaten in the North America stakes by Columbus, though it now seems likely that explorers from Bristol beat both in the crossing of the Atlantic. From Elizabethan to Georgian times, the legitimate wealth of Poole was based on fishing for cod in the chilly waters of the Grand Banks. As foreign competitors entered the arena, Poole developed a safer if less glamorous trade, shipping clay from nearby deposits to the Potteries.

The **Isle of Purbeck** was not an island but the fiefdom of Corfe Castle. In this section of the coast much wealth and employment was created by the quarrying of top-grade limestones. Corfe and Langton Matravers were noted medieval quarrying villages, and Swanage was the harbour from which the Purbeck building stone and false marble were exported. Fortunately for **Swanage**, new quarries had just been opened at the time when London experienced its Great Fire. Then, in Victorian times, two related families of local stone merchants sponsored its development as a resort. They were heavily involved in rebuilding bits of London and as a result Swanage acquired an assortment of façades, monuments and statuary which was rescued during demolition and re-erected here. In the mid-1980s the town experienced a bitter confrontation between locals and property developers seeking to build their 'Unashamedly upmarket' yacht haven. At the last moment The House of Lords threw out plans for a concrete breakwater and private berths in the haven.

At and around **Lulworth Cove** there are fine passages of coastal scenery, scenery which must have been much more remarkable

Lulworth Cove, once a haven for smugglers

before the army depopulated East Lulworth to create training grounds and the unsightly car parks brought people-pollution. The prohibited and over-visited areas stand side by side, with the fossilised stumps of an ancient forest which flourished on a river delta standing on the margins of the no-go area. The Cove, cut into the Wealden Clay after the sea breached the coastal ridge of Portland stone, could not offer a safe anchorage when the winds blew strongly from the south, but it was often used by privateers. At Durdle Door a spectacular arch has been carved in the Portland ridge and Bat's Head is a noble promontory.

After **Melcombe** and **Weymouth** we come to the **Isle of Portland**, where the quarrying theme is resumed. For beneath the Purbeck rubble there are thick beds of the finest limestone, which was quarried and shipped out to form some of the grandest buildings in Georgian and Victorian London. Earlier, in the days of Sir Christopher Wren, the quarrymen of Portland successfully defended their claim to the stone when it was suggested that it was the property of the Crown. It was exported from the Stone Quay beside Henry VIII's Portland Castle. Quarrying still dominates the landscape. The artificial harbour, guarded by three

The quarrying of top-class building stone continues on the Isle of Portland

massive breakwaters, was built in the 1840s by convicts awaiting transportation to Australia.

The Isle is joined to the mainland by **Chesil Beach**, a storm beach of shingle around 26 km (16 miles) long, 150 m to 180 m (500 to 600 feet) wide and in places more than 12 m (40 feet) high, where the sea has graded the pebbles by rolling the smallest stones north-westwards during southerly gales. It continues to the medieval port of **Lyme Regis**, where the geological interest is maintained by the cliffs which are packed with the fossilised shells of ammonites, which died about 200 million years ago. This was the only harbour between Portland Sound and the Exe, and some time around 1300, it was protected by a curving breakwater, known as The Cobb, which was built to the west of the port. The frequent breaching of The Cobb by storms, combined with French raiding, caused Lyme's trade to decline, although the breakwater was rebuilt in Elizabethan times.

Beyond **Sidmouth**, a genteel resort guarded by cliffs of red marl, lie **Exmouth** and **Teignmouth**. Exmouth is noted for the circular house 'A la Ronde', dating from 1798 and built with a shell gallery in the manner of the church of San Vitale, Ravenna. Along with Exmouth, Teignmouth seems to be one of the oldest resorts in Devon. Teignmouth was burned by the French in 1340, but by the 1820s had become the port used for the export of Devon granite. By the middle of the eighteenth century it had emerged as a popular resort. Further still are **Tor Bay** and **Torquay**. Torquay has boasted two unusual tourist attractions: Kent's Cavern, where the caves in the limestone were occupied by human families more than 100,000 years ago, and Napoleon. Defeated at Waterloo in 1815, and hunted by his countrymen, the Emperor surrendered to the British blockading squadron off Rochefort. He was held captive on the *Bellerophon*, which anchored in Tor Bay for several weeks, and those who came to stare and wave did much to breathe life into the emerging resort.

Brixham was the port of entry for William of Orange when he arrived in 1688 to take the crown of England. Since most were quite glad to see him, this hardly rates as a successful invasion. In Norman times, a village developed by a tiny estuary which was later engulfed by the town, and the villagers used drift nets to fish for herring, while in the seventeenth century, Brixham pioneered new fishing techniques. Trawling was developed here, and the Brixham boats fished the Grand Banks. It is said that the fishermen brought back the powerful Newfoundland dogs which were then used to haul the boats ashore in bad weather. Later, they copied cutters of a Dutch type and began to exploit trawling grounds in the Channel and North Sea. Then, in the 1870s, they developed the famous two-masted Brixham trawler, which was fast yet able to work in rough weather. Part of the catch from Brixham and other West Country ports was dried and exported from Dartmouth, which had received wine shipments from Bordeaux until England lost control of this outpost in 1453. This caused a slump in trade until the exploitation of the Grand Banks fishery at the start of the sixteenth century.

Just to the north of **Start Point** are the ruins of Hallsands village, which perished in 1917, after dredgers had removed the shingle protecting the beach for use in building works at Plymouth harbour. Between the promontories of Bolt Head and Prawle Point is **Salcombe** harbour, where the drowned valley would form an excellent natural haven were it not for the sand bar which runs across its entrance. **Plymouth** has no such drawback, for the drowned valleys of the Plym and Tamar form a magnificent harbour. At first it was the Tamar which attracted shipping, and boats turning into the estuary and anchoring at Saltash were sheltered from southerly gales; later it became more the fashion to turn to the north-east and shelter in the mouth of the Plym. Under the patronage of the monks of nearby Plympton, Plymouth grew as a fishing village and as a port which exported wool and tin and imported the wines of Bordeaux. It also became notorious on the continent as a lair for pirates – most of the national heroes which we associate with Plymouth were primarily pirates, and not ashamed to be such. The Royal Dockyard of Plymouth was founded in 1689, becoming Devonport in 1824. With a population of almost a quarter of a million, Plymouth is by far the largest coastal town of the south-west. Particularly since the Reformation, it flourished on pugnacity and the national dread of invasion, but now, with the navy greatly reduced and the fate of the Devonport naval dockyards in question, its future is less assured. But whatever the future may hold, the historical legacy of Drake, Hawkins, Grenville and Raleigh will never be forgotten, even if it is often distorted.

Cawsand also has skeletons in its cupboard, these being the bones of the smugglers who went about their affairs within hailing distance of the great naval base, though enjoying the seclusion provided by Picklecombe Point. The Cornish ports of Looe, **Fowey** and Falmouth all have harbours situated where rivers have gouged their courses into fault lines in the earth's crust. As the coastguards became more proficient and the taxes levied on imports were reduced, so smuggling declined – and the rise of Cornish tourism did as much for failed smugglers as it did for the fishermen – though generally they were one and the same. It has been estimated that in 1770 the loss of state revenues as a result of smuggling amounted to £150,000 – an enormous sum in those days both to the authorities and the beneficiaries. In 1824, Mayor Bennet of Fowey dumped much of his contraband brandy into the harbour to avoid prosecution, but he was still found to have £300-worth of illicit liquor left in his house.

The harbour at Looe

Before its smugglers, Fowey had its 'gallants', pirates who were as bad as any on the south coast. They were unsullied by chauvinism and attacked English shipping with the same zest that they vented on foreign vessels. But Fowey was also successful in more legitimate fields, and was one of the leading ports engaged in the medieval trade with Bordeaux. Early in this century, it supported a fine fleet of Atlantic schooners, until U-boat attacks during the 1914–18 war accounted for most of these sailing vessels. Along with little Par, nearby, it still exports kaolin or rotted granite from the china clay works around St Austell. Mevagissey became a

fishing port at the start of the fifteenth century and gained improved harbour defences in the 1860s during the heyday of the pilchard industry.

With its harbour defended by the artillery castles of Pendennis and Mawes, which were built by Henry VIII in the 1540s, **Falmouth** emerged as a mail packet station at the end of the seventeenth century, with overseas mail from the capital being brought to the port overland, avoiding the natural hazards and piracy in the Channel. With the coming of the railway and the steamship, the packet trade was lost to Southampton in the 1850s

Mevagissey was once known as 'fishy-gissey', but now pleasure craft outnumber the remaining fishing boats

211

but new activities in repairing, servicing and cleaning ships were developed. Today, the Carrick Road leading to Falmouth Harbour is populated by pleasure craft and laid-up tankers.

Although the real old Cornish capacities for piracy and smuggling were probably the equals of the myths, the indulgence in wrecking has been greatly exaggerated. It was one thing to pick over cargoes shed by a storm-struck vessel and another to lure a ship deliberately to the rocks. Even so, when a beacon was erected on **Lizard Point** in 1619, the locals were less than delighted. At least Parson Troutbeck in Scilly was being honest when he prayed: 'Dear God, we pray not that wrecks should happen, but if it be Thy will that they do, we pray Thee let them be to the benefit of Thy poor people of Scilly.' Westward of The Lizard, the most striking coastal feature is **St Michael's Mount**, an offshore granite boss which can be reached by a causeway from Marazion at low water. The Mount appears to have been visited by Mediterranean traders in prehistoric times; the Greek explorer, Pytheas, may have come here around 300 BC, and the Cornish tin trade was mentioned by Diodorus Siculus in the second century BC. Much later, it was haunted by seamen of a different kind, and in 1750 the army was sent to attend to thugs from the hamlets of Breage and Germoe near Helston who were plundering a storm-damaged vessel taking shelter behind the Mount.

Nearby is **Penzance**, which emerged as a fishing and trading port in the latter part of the Middle Ages, and then grew as a centre for the exporting of tin and the catching of pilchards, until these activities declined in the second half of the nineteenth century. Newlyn captured the local fishing trade but Penzance discovered a future as a tourist centre. As a railhead town blessed with a mellow oceanic climate and proximity to such scenic attractions as Land's End and St Michael's Mount, the palm-decked resort could scarcely fail.

And so to **Land's End**. Nature has done her best to bring England to a splendid conclusion, with noble cliffs worked into columns and battlements as the winds and waves have worked on the joints in the granite. What the masses of mankind have done is another matter.

Noble granite cliffs at Land's End

213

Chapter Ten

FROM LAND'S END TO JOHN O'GROAT'S

The west coast of Britain is remembered for its bold cliffs of hard rock and for rugged shores lashed by Atlantic waves. It is also a coastline of contrasts, for it includes expanses of dunes and famous links golf courses, great sea lochs, estuaries and sandy beaches. It contains several of our largest ports, Bristol, Liverpool and Glasgow, although, unlike the Channel coast, there is not the great profusion of active and decaying little ports all competing for life like fleas along a pulsing vein.

The north Cornish coast is treacherous and unforgiving, a place of cramped bays and 'yawns' eroded along fault lines bracketed by towering headlands of dark rock. Many of these headlands were defended by ramparts and rock-cut ditches to serve as cliff castles during the Iron Age. Gurnard's Head is a good example, while around the hamlet of Zennor one can see field patterns little changed from those which the cliff castle dwellers knew. Geological history is also much in evidence, for above the cliff bastions of the Penwith peninsula, a level land surface at a height of 230 m to 250 m (750 to 800 feet) is plain to see, a relic of a marine surface which was cut flat countless millions of years ago. Above the cliffs, another ancient wave-cut platform is displayed at heights of 110 m to 140 m (350 to 430 feet). Although the present cliff line seems defiant and immovable, these uplifted marine erosion surfaces remind us of the transient nature of even the most durable facets of our world.

Harder still than the granite of Land's End is the greenstone of Penwith, displayed in the cliffs at Cape Cornwall, Gurnard's Head, Zennor Head and the Island at St Ives. The story of **St Ives** is typical of several Cornish fishing ports, and is preserved in the landscape in the improved harbour facilities of the 1860s and the dwellings built above the old fish cellars which now exist as tourist shops and cafés. Pretty as a picture, St Ives was discovered and colonised by artists at the end of the Victorian era. Above Lelant on the silting estuary of the Hayle there is a much older settlement, evidenced by the hut circles visible within the ramparts of the Iron Age fort on Trencrom Hill. Portreath was an old importing centre for timber and coal, while the copper mines around St Day and Scorrier were served by a horse-drawn gravity tramway from Poldice to Portreath. St Agnes Beacon is a domed granite

Previous page:
All that remains of
the Cornish port of
Portquin

boss, and here relics of a tin-mining landscape dating from Victorian and Edwardian times are preserved. Attempts to build a harbour to serve the local tin and copper mines at Trevaunance Cove were thwarted by the power of the sea storms on this coast. A relic of a quite different age lies in the sands near **Perranporth**. Here the cell or oratory of the Irish missionary saint, St Piran, survives as the oldest remaining chapel in the south-west. Thought to date from the sixth or seventh century, it was built of slate and granite rubble bound by clay, with stone benches facing a small altar inside. Before it could experience an enlargement and rebuilding in the early medieval centuries it was entombed by wind-driven sands and preserved. Nearby there stands a Dark Age cross. Now, this is more a place for action than contemplation and Perran Bay is favoured by surfers, for the deep waters allow the great Atlantic breakers to approach the shore with undiminished power.

At **Newquay**, the nineteenth-century railhead tourist town sits beside the more venerable successor to the fourteenth-century fishing hamlet of Towan Blustry. Mention has already been made of the huer's look-out house which stands nearby on Towan Head. During the heyday of the pilchard fishery, and until the early years of this century, such posts were manned in August by huers who gazed seawards in search of the reddish patches which were pilchard shoals. On hearing the cry 'Hevva!' the fishermen below would sail to the place indicated by the huer and encircle the shoal in a long seine net as their comrades, the 'lurkers', beat the waves with their oars to drive the pilchards towards the trap. Then, the netted catch was hauled to shoreline and pulled up on the beach. To the north of Newquay, Bedruthan Steps is a spectacular assemblage of stacks and islets carved by the blind artistry of the sea. In legend the stacks were carved as stepping stones by the giant whose name they bear. Now the romance is eroded, for the place is so popular that matting is needed to protect the cliff path from the thousands of trampling feet. Further north are the bold greenstone headlands of Park Head and Trevose Head.

Padstow benefited from the silting of the Camel estuary, which caused trade to shift downstream from Wadebridge. When Leland visited Padstow around 1540, he found a fishing port which was good and lively, 'but uncleanly kept'. In the centuries which followed, its neighbour upstream experienced mounting difficulties as the Doom Bar grew across the estuary. According to local legend, this was an act of vengeance for the mermaid who was shot by one Long Tom Yeo of Padstow. In the nineteenth century, Padstow grew rapidly, gaining shipbuilding industries and becoming a harbour of refuge on this dangerous coast. The railway arrived in 1899, and, as navigational difficulties by then affected Padstow, it allowed tourism to offset the decline in the town's maritime affairs. Although attracting many tourists, the town's May Day ceremonies are genuine, lusty and of uncertain origins. They involve two prancing hobby horses, the Red Ribbon 'Oss and the Blue Ribbon 'Oss, the former symbolic of pagan fertility and resurrection rites and the latter spawned by Victorian prudery. They also involve a song sung with great fervour:

> Unite and unite, and let us all unite,
> For summer is a-come unto day;
> And whither we are going we will all unite
> In the merry morning of May.

Along the coast from Rumps Point, with its Iron Age cliff castle, and the failed port of Portquin is **Port Isaac**, not as picturesque as some other fishing ports, but one of the earliest and one which preserves an old street pattern of narrow alleys. Next comes **Tintagel**, pretty and interesting enough not to need to be plagued by a myth-pedalling industry. Less visited is **Boscastle**, with the only secure natural harbour on this rugged coast between Padstow and Bude. The inner jetty was built by Sir Richard Grenville in 1584, and the port was still active in the nineteenth century, when slate was exported. Then comes **Bude**, which existed as a hamlet with a chapel at the end of the Middle Ages and gained a small quay and artificial harbour in Elizabethan times. It got off to an early start in the tourist industry, and at the time of the Napoleonic wars some cottages were built here to cater for visitors attracted by the sea bathing. From Bude northwards into Devon the coast is rocky and devoid of shelter from westerly gales.

The great rock wall of **Hartland Point** was known to the Romans as the Promontory of Hercules; it helps to shelter the fossilised fishing village of Clovelly. Replication rather than preservation is the theme at Appledore at the mouth of the Taw–Torridge estuary, for Hink's boatyard here has reproduced historic vessels ranging from Roman galleys to Drake's *Golden Hind*. Upstream, silting has robbed the old ports of Bideford and Barnstaple of their traffic. Boats still ply around Appledore, taking their chance with the dreaded sandbanks of the Bideford Bar; once the port sent boats to the Grand Banks and imported tobacco from Virginia. Just across the estuary at Braunton Burrows is one of the finest expanses of rolling coastal dunes, bound by marram grass and fringed by sea holly and sea stock. In this Nature Conservancy Council reserve there is the full range of dune habitats, from open sand to thick scrub, while the slacks support yellow iris, stinking iris and viper's-bugloss. Out to sea lies Lundy Island, once a stronghold of smugglers and pirates, but now the abode of sea-birds and, since 1986, Britain's first Statutory Marine Nature Reserve.

The resort of **Ilfracombe** has a strong nautical tradition and at one time during the last century more than seventy vessels were owned here, and there was a flourishing shipyard. The north-facing coast near Ilfracombe is no less treacherous than the north Cornish coast, but at **Lynton** disaster came from a different quarter. Having neither grown nor shrunk very much for a thou-sand years, Lynton, partnered by its little fishing port of **Lynmouth**, became a tourist centre in the nineteenth century, and the townscape is redolent of the Victorian era. In the August of 1953, Exmoor became saturated by driving rain until a torrent flooded down from the moor, bursting from the watercourses and sending a wall of boulder-charged water 3 m (10 feet) high through Lynmouth. Walls were smashed by the boulders and dwellings entombed in the mud. Here fifteen residents were killed, while the total number of fatalities in the locality was thirty-four. But the folk of Lynmouth came from a hardy stock; during a storm in 1899 the local fishermen were unable to launch their lifeboat, but the villagers and crew manhandled it up steep slopes and down narrow lanes, driving it overland for 21 km (13 miles) to launch from Porlock eleven hours later, and so accompany the *Forrest Hall* to a safe anchorage across the Bristol Channel.

From **Foreland Point** to **Porlock Bay** the wooded edge of Exmoor falls steeply to the **Bristol Channel**, though the terrain is such that the scenery of hogsback cliffs here is seen at its best from the sea. During the Dark Ages, Celtic missionaries from Wales crossed the Channel to gain converts and they are remembered in some of the church dedications, such as the one to Bueno at Culbone, and to Dubricius, who was Bishop of Llandaff around 520, at Porlock. Safe anchorages along the Exmoor coast were few, and while Lynmouth and Porlock Weir handled local produce, larger cargoes were shipped at Ilfracombe, Minehead and Watchet. Squire Luttrell built a good quay at **Minehead** in 1616,

The tiny church of Culbone on the wooded Exmoor cliffs

and in the next century the port was used by ships bound for Newfoundland, and by traders bringing woollen yarn from Ireland; this was sold at Dunster yarn market to the local weavers. The town is now the main resort in West Somerset, although the redevelopment of the shopping centre is thought by many to have spoiled some of its character. **Watchet** was the port used for the export of iron ore mined in the Brendon Hills and shipped across the Channel to Welsh ports like Newport. At Kilve there is a gem of a beach, with a marine platform cut across dipping beds, and cliffs of Lias packed with ammonite fossils like currants in a cake. Above the cliff are lime kilns where the rock was reduced.

The shores of the Bristol Channel can bring delight and despair to the wildlife enthusiast. The oozes of **Bridgwater Bay** are rich in marine life and attract diverse flocks of waders and ducks. It is one of two great moulting grounds visited by shelduck for the period when they become flightless and vulnerable. But there are nuclear reactors above the Severn Bridge at **Berkeley** and **Oldbury** and

The little harbour at Portlock Weir

two below it at **Hinkley Point** beside the bay, while noxious waste from oil refineries, chemicals plants and other industries pollutes the tapering Channel. The waters contain exceptionally high concentrations of cadmium, zinc and lead, and the nuclear stations discharge contaminated cooling water. Such concerns, however, are not obvious to windswept ramblers on the narrow, lofty limestone peninsula of **Brean Down**, with its relics of ancient fields and settlement, its rare colony of white rockrose and views southwards across the reclaimed marshland of Berrow and the

Ammonite fossils abound in the cliffs of blue Lias at Kilve

Somerset Levels and north-eastwards towards Weston-super-Mare. Between Weston and Bristol is the staid resort of **Clevedon**, its front punctuated by evergreen trees which have been trained to grow at diagonals to the horizon by the unhampered blast from the prevailing westerlies as they rip across the open waters of the Channel.

Bristol, near the estuary of the Avon, has been a great port since Saxon times. During the Middle Ages, Bristol traded with Ireland, exported the cloth produced in its hinterland to Gascony, Portugal and Spain and imported the wines of these places. The river port was approached through a constricted gorge, which assisted defence but which caused navigational problems as the size of ships increased during the Middle Ages, so that they had to be towed into harbour. During the fifteenth century, the Cabots settled in Bristol and helped to awaken the city to the possibilities of trans-Atlantic trading. At the close of the Middle Ages, the port's traditional commerce was declining, but the New World offered fresh challenges. Then, the reputation of Bristol became sullied by the association with the slave trade. Perhaps it was the privateer, John Hawkins, who pioneered this shameful commerce in Elizabethan times. The prevailing ocean winds were employed in a triangular trade, taking metal and textile goods to West Africa, then taking aboard a sad human cargo for sale in the Spanish colonies of the West Indies, and returning to Bristol with molasses, sugar and tobacco.

At a time when Southampton was said to be 'almost forsook and neglected' as London captured its continental trade in the seventeenth and eighteenth centuries, Bristol was prospering from its links with different continents. In 1696 the diarist, Celia Fiennes, wrote that 'the town is a very great trading city as most in England, and is esteemed the largest next London.' Early in the nineteenth century, the navigational problems at Bristol were resolved with the construction of a 'floating harbour', with gates to pen back the waters as the tide fell – a costly project which raised the harbour rates at Bristol above those at Liverpool and Hull. Bristol emerged as an Atlantic passenger port in Georgian times, and in 1864 Brunel completed his famous suspension bridge across the Avon gorge at Clifton. The city had been a major international port for centuries, but in the course of the Victorian era, it gradually lost its place to Liverpool. In this century, how-ever, Bristol has proved far better equipped to survive the decline of Atlantic sea trading. After the abolition of the slave trade, better commercial links with West Africa were developed, and the town enjoyed the advantages of the improved docks opened at Avonmouth and Portishead in 1880.

The horn-shaped outline of the **Severn estuary** has a great effect upon the tides, for while seemingly endless expanses of mud are exposed at low water, at high tide they are swiftly submerged as the inrush of water is funnelled towards the mouth of the river. The tidal effect rushes upstream at speeds which are sometimes in excess of 16 km (10 miles) per hour, and which are still evident at

Gloucester. Under exceptional conditions the 'bore' can even reach Tewkesbury, a good 32 km (20 miles) upstream from the outlet. The estuary has always been a great barrier to movement between Wales and the south-west of England, and over the centuries countless people perished in the surging tide as they attempted to sail across the constricted channel at low water. In 1966, the suspension bridge was opened and travel assumed a quite different complexion.

On the Welsh side of the estuary change has been heaped upon change. Lands which had sent their missionary saints across the water to convert the speakers of pagan English were invaded and colonised in Norman times. A chain of castle-guarded market towns was established, where communities of English and Flemish traders operated within the partly pacified countrysides. Then, during the nineteenth century, South Wales experienced all the clamour and trauma of industrialisation as coal trains streamed out of the valley mines to the coal ports at **Barry**, **Newport** and **Cardiff**. Newport was founded by the Normans and gained a stone castle early in the thirteenth century. It grew to be one of the largest Welsh boroughs in the early fourteenth century, but then declined. It was burned by Glyndwr in 1402 and damaged by Cromwell in 1648. Newport grew again rapidly in the early nineteenth century with the construction of the Monmouth and Brecon Canals. The Romans first built at Cardiff at the end of the first century, and this site was later occupied by a Norman motte and by a thirteenth-century castle. Cardiff may have been a Viking slave-finding port, but the town seems to have been developed in the 1180s during Norman colonisation. Burned by the Welsh in 1185, it became the largest town in Wales during the thirteenth century. It was burned again by Glyndwr in 1404 and did not recover its medieval size until the early nineteenth century. Further along the coast is **Swansea**, which began as a little Viking trading station and became a Norman castle town and the administrative centre for the Gower. Yet even in the early nineteenth century, the settlement, which had been walled five centuries earlier, existed merely as a cluster of houses at the mouth and west bank of the River Tawe. Then the town erupted with the growth of the coal trade, and a metal exchange was established. In the area known as the Strand, to the rear of the castle, the medieval quay of Swansea was discovered in 1953.

One by one the pits have closed, leaving behind the dereliction of heavy industries which nobody seems to need any more.

The Pembrokeshire coast near Lydstep Head

Slimmer, and in some cases smarter than before, the ports of South Wales now scour the horizon for new opportunities.

With Swansea and Llanelli to either side of its neck, the **Gower peninsula** provides a surprising contrast to the adjacent industrialised areas, and a foretaste of the scenic splendour of the Dyfed (Pembrokeshire) coast. Here too, there are fine dune systems at **Oxwich**, which enclose peaty fen and reed beds. First we come to **Tenby**, a resort with elegant Georgian terraces and a history which goes much deeper. It was established as a Norman base and developed as a planned castle town in the thirteenth century. At the end of the Middle Ages, it was described by Leland: 'Tenby is a walled town hard on the Severn Sea in Pembrokeshire. There is a cove and a pier made for ships, it stands on a main rock but not very high, and the Severn Sea so gulfeth in about it, that at full sea almost the third part of the town is enclosed by water.' The town walls were built after 1328, and improved in 1457, and so much of the circuit survives that Tenby is of exceptional interest to historians.

The Pembrokeshire Coast National Park was created in 1952, in recognition of the scenic splendour surrounding the area which was so heavily colonised by the English during the Middle Ages that it became known as 'little England beyond Wales'. Much of the fascination in the section to the south of Tenby derives from the geological detail, with rapidly alternating beds of limestone, grit and sandstone, while around and to the north of **St Brides Bay**, ancient rocks with volcanic intrusions are carved into cliffs and inlets. Sculpted by the sea, these rocks form magnificent features, including sea stacks, such as Elegug Stacks on the Castlemartin peninsula, arches, like the Green Bridge of Wales, rias, like Solva harbour, while the remains of submerged forests at Wiseman's Bridge, Manorbier and Newgale all add to the interest. The scenic history of the coast is complex; inland there are traces of benches and fossil cliffs, which were carved during interglacial periods, when the sea stood much higher than today, while the land is grooved by channels cut by torrents of meltwater as the glaciers receded.

Near St Govan's Head on the Pembrokeshire coast

Milford Haven estuary, a broad drowned river valley

With its exceptional coastal scenery, a wealth of historical interest and a richness in wildlife, exemplified by the seabird colonies on Skomer and Skokholm islands and the grey seal breeding ground beneath the cliffs on Ramsey Island, this would seem to be an unspoilt coastal paradise. But this is not quite the case. During the 1950s and 1960s the great ria of **Milford Haven**, regarded by Nelson as the finest natural harbour in Britain, was developed as a deep-water oil port and refinery centre. By 1974, it had five oil terminals and four refineries, and it had emerged as Britain's largest port in terms of tonnage and cargo handled. The existence of such a facility so close to some of our most important seabird sanctuaries and finest beaches is a constant source of concern.

Even in such an area of breathtaking natural scenery, the historical legacy is too important to be overlooked. There is St Govan's chapel, built into the cliffs near Bosherton in the thirteenth century beside the cleft where a hermit is said to have lived around seven centuries earlier. Wells within and beside the chapel were said to have healing powers. **Pembroke** was built on a ridge of limestone flanked by the Pembroke river, an arm of Milford Haven. The Normans captured the area in 1093, and Pembroke was developed as an impregnable castle town with a planned layout. By the Tudor period, Pembroke had expanded beyond its medieval walls, but then it began to decline as its military importance diminished and its maritime trade was lost to Haverfordwest. The armoured splendour of Pembroke Castle is matched by the ecclesiastical magnificence of St David's cathedral. Above the cliffs nearby there is a ruined chapel dedicated to St Non, the mother of St David. A Celtic religious community may have been established here by St David in the sixth century, and the present cathedral was begun about 1180. It was enlarged and modified in the course of the Middle Ages, but allowed to become almost derelict during the eighteenth and nineteenth centuries, until Sir Gilbert Scott supervised a restoration and reconstruction. During the Middle Ages, St David's became a significant centre of pilgrimage, and this stimulated the growth of the nearby town, which carried out its trade from Porth Clais and which declined at the close of the period.

Fishguard was a Norman foundation, but its history thereafter was undistinguished and, at the start of the nineteenth century, it was still restricted to a huddle of dwellings above the hogsback cliffs guarding the bay. Still, there were moments of excitement; during the American War of Independence, John Paul Jones sailed in, captured a merchant ship in the bay and loosed-off two broadsides at the town. This was also the scene of the last invasion of Britain for, in 1797, a French force, 1,400-strong, was landed nearby with orders to incite rebellion as they marched on Liverpool. However, the troops, many of them convicts, thought it a better idea to get drunk while they sat around waiting to be captured. Those now arriving in the Irish Sea ferries are made of sterner stuff.

The headland of **Dinas Head**, which juts between the bays of Fishguard and Newport, is made of ancient rocks rich in the remains of primitive corals and sea urchins. **Cardigan** stands at the mouth of the Teifi, renowned as a salmon river in the Middle Ages and one where coracles of timeless design can still be seen being paddled by those fishermen with the hereditary right to fish with a net slung between two of the craft. Cardigan gives its name to the great bay which sweeps northwards to the Llyn peninsula. The Norman castle town was created on the north bank of the Teifi estuary in the reign of Henry I, and during the troubled years which followed it was taken by the Welsh on several occasions. Cardigan grew during the thirteenth and fourteenth centuries but, in 1600, it was said to be 'ruinous and decayed'. Later in the century, the maritime trade revived and the town grew again; the gaps in the townscape were filled, but the layout of medieval streets survives to this day.

At **Cemaes Head**, guarding the western flank of the Teifi estuary, ancient mudstones of the Ordovician era are contorted in great folds which illustrate more clearly than any textbook diagram the majestic power of the earth forces. North of New Quay the coast assumes a smoother form, though passages of rugged scenery still occur. **Cormorant Rock**, near Aberystwyth, is an unusual and striking sea stack, with a pyramidical profile which has been cut in the alternating beds of grit and shale. They are so steeply tilted that they outcrop at an angle of about 60 degrees from the horizontal.

Aberystwyth, founded in the reign of Edward I, is situated where the Rivers Rheidol and Ystwyth converge upon Cardigan Bay. The earlier English settlements in the area were further inland, but in 1277 Edmund, Earl of Lancaster, the king's brother, chose to abandon them in favour of a new castle town and walled borough at the coast. Medieval Aberystwyth was largely destroyed by Cromwell's troops in 1647. Rapid growth did not take place until the nineteenth century, with the development of lead mining and slate quarrying and the exploitation of the herring fishery. By the 1830s, there were more than 130 vessels registered at Aberystwyth, and the town had taken over Cardigan's role as the leading west-coast port in Wales. This growth was consolidated by the tourist industry, and Aberystwyth became known, rather inaptly, as the Welsh Brighton. Cliffs of steeply tilted ancient mudstones tower over the sea to the north of the town, and at Borth there are traces of a forest which was submerged during, or a little before, the Bronze Age.

As we follow the bay northwards we find a fascinating alternation of forms of coastal scenery, with cliffs, such as the ones south of Fairbourne, vast, sandy forelands backed by dunes, as at Morfa Dyffryn, lagoons and shingle beaches, as at the Dysynni estuary near Tywyn, estuarine mud-flats and spits. The mouth of the **Mawddach estuary** to the south of Barmouth is partly closed by the bar formed by the pebble and sand ridge of Ro Wen, in the shelter of which sand-flats and salt-marshes have developed. At Llandanwg in the coastal desert of Morfa Dyffryn, a chapel stands partly engulfed in the shifting sand.

Harlech provides a dramatic illustration of the impermanent nature of the coastline. The castle was built by Edward I in 1286, as part of his strategy of ringing rebellious North Wales with royal castles of the most modern and formidable kind. A planned borough was built beside the castle, but it scarcely recovered from the burning by Glyndwr in 1404 which destroyed forty-six houses. Harlech was a port, and the castle was built on a rocky knoll above the shore, allowing it to be supplied from the sea in the event of a siege. Yet now the sea lies far away, for the pebble spit of Morfa Harlech has advanced northwards and seawards to surround the former island of **Llanvigangel-y-Traethau**. Just across the water is **Porthmadog**, created in the middle of the nineteenth century as the port for the export of Snowdonian slate, used in the Victorian reroofing of much of England, with expanses of mud-flat being reclaimed and embanked to allow the quarry railways to reach the margin of Tremadog Bay.

Possibly the most peculiar village in Wales is **Portmeirion**, where, in 1925, the architect, Sir Clough Williams-Ellis, attempted to create a Mediterranean fishing port packed with seventeenth- and eighteenth-century Italianate architecture. The visible scene at this holiday village is anything but Welsh. And the climate is anything but Mediterranean – but it is all good fun.

Next comes **Criccieth**, a castle town created by Edward I to control the bay and coast road. A Welsh castle already existed on the cliff-girt promontory. The planned English settlement failed to expand despite the opportunities for maritime trade, and its burning by Glyndwr in 1404 stemmed the modest growth. At the end of the Middle Ages, the town was reduced to a decaying hamlet, and at the start of the nineteenth century it was described as a village and 'a most wretched place'.

Pwllheli existed as a Welsh settlement flanked by dunes on the southern shores of the Llyn peninsula before Edward transformed the pattern of settlement in the region. It was a small sea port, and its boats fished for herring in Cardigan Bay. Low-lying and prone to flooding by the sea, Pwllheli was destroyed by enemies coming from another quarter, being devastated by the followers of Glyndwr at the start of the fifteenth century. Only an influx of new settlers allowed the little town to survive.

The **Llyn peninsula** offers scenic and historical interest in equal measure. The towering summit of Yr Eifl is a prominent landmark, and on one of the neighbouring hilltops lie the remains of the Iron Age and Romano–British 'town' of Tre'r Ceiri, the dwellings lying within a still massive rampart of drystone walling. The coast here is scarred somewhat by granite quarrying, but near

The remains of the coastal quarrying village of Porth-y-Nant

Nefyn, a cliff path leads down to the abandoned quarry village of Porth-y-Nant, now redeveloped as a centre for the regeneration of the Welsh language. Nearby, guarded by the headland of Carreg Ddu, the bay of Porth Dinllaen was once considered as the site for a ferry port to serve as an alternative to Holyhead. Moving northwards again, the coastal scenery becomes less dramatic and is composed of low cliffs of boulder clay, dumped by the great Snowdonian glaciers, and of dunes and boulder-strewn beaches.

Caernarfon is another Edwardian castle town which was built close to the site of the Roman fort of Segontium in the years after 1283. The walls of the borough enclosed a peninsula beside the **Menai Strait** bounded by the Rivers Seiont and Cadnant. The great castle guarded the southern end of the strait and served as an administrative centre for North Wales. In the nineteenth century, Caernarfon became an important port for the export of slate quarried in the mountains of Snowdonia. In 1294, Edward became convinced of the need for a castle to control the northern end of the strait, and so Beaumaris was built on the Anglesey shore. The level marshland site allowed the adoption of a symmetrical concentric layout without the need for concessions to terrain, and the castle was provided with its own harbour facilities. The walled town established beside the castle became a successful seaport with its own fleet of herring boats.

On **Anglesey**, the highest cliffs are found in the vicinity of the picturesque South Stack lighthouse just west of the ferry port of Holyhead. On the slopes above the cliffs are the remains of the dwellings of some of the earliest-known of our coastal populations. Early in the Bronze Age, a sprawling village of more than fifty farmsteads grew here, with new homes being added as more land was cleared of stones and as the older dwellings were abandoned. At Newborough Warren in the south-west of the island there is one of Britain's most extensive surviving dune systems. Afforestation has reduced the area of interest, but rare orchids still flourish in the damp slacks.

Returning to the mainland coast, **Bangor** differs from its neighbours, for it is not a planned medieval castle town but a much older centre with origins associated with a monastery of the sixth century which became the ecclesiastical focus of North Wales. During the Middle Ages, the market at Bangor competed with that at Caernarfon, but the town remained quite small until the end of the eighteenth century, when it grew rapidly as an outlet for the slate industry.

Conwy has retained its medieval circuit of walls and provides a striking insight on Edward I's vision for Wales. It was founded in 1283 on a spur of land flanked by the River Conwy to the east and the Afon Gyffin to the south. Though furnished with a port, Conwy never made much of a mark as a maritime centre. It is known firstly for its castle and secondly for Telford's suspension bridge, which bestrides the river once dominated only by Edward's stronghold. The popular resort towns of the north Welsh coast have already been explored, and so we return to England via the estuarine mud-flats of the River Dee. These are renowned as a wintering ground for waders and receive enormous populations of oystercatcher, dunlin and knot. Grey seals bask here in summer, and dolphins can sometimes be glimpsed offshore.

In May 1991, the government warned anglers not to eat fish

The Conwy estuary looking towards the Little Orme and Llandudno junction

caught in the polluted **Mersey estuary**, for by eating fish contaminated by high levels of mercury and PCBs (polychlorinated biphenyls) they risked damage to their livers and nervous systems. But a spokesman for the anglers pointed out that many of them were unemployed, and the poisoned fish were their cheapest source of food. This sad story symbolises the plight of **Liverpool**, a proud city which has lost its way and where the monuments to former greatness loom over the filthy waterways and derelict acres. By the end of the seventeenth century Liverpool had risen to a position where it rivalled Bristol as the second seaport of the kingdom. Both ports faced west, and both grew rich on the proceeds of the notorious triangular trade in slaves and American goods. But as the cotton industry developed, Liverpool was better placed to serve the mill towns which mushroomed in the damp northern air along the canals between Leeds and the Mersey. Fortunes were founded on sorrow: the wretchedness of the slaves in the cotton plantations of the Deep South, the poverty of the children toiling from dawn to dusk in the mills and the hardship of the Irish and European refugees who arrived in Liverpool to secure steerage passages in the stinking holds of emigrant ships bound for the New World. Yet the city had a proud countenance and boasted the best docks in Georgian and Victorian England, the great Cammell-Laird shipyards at Birkenhead, the majestic headquarters of the Cunard line and the great edifice of the Royal Liver Insurance Building. The steady decline of the docks began quite early in the present century and, while new industry was established, Liverpool still seems unable to comprehend or cope with the loss of the maritime industries which fuelled its growth.

Just across the estuary is **New Brighton**, and at the start of the Beatles era, six ferries plied back and forth, bringing up to half a million Liverpudlians a day to this hard-bitten resort. Young girls who came on these boats and played on the beach are now mothers – and they will not allow their children to set foot on those sands, which are now fouled by all manner of urban and industrial filth. The sources of the poisons are apparently known and obvious to all but those with the power to call a halt.

The coast to the north of the Mersey estuary is not short of pollution – but neither is it short of sand. There are dunes, links golf courses, sandy beaches which seem to extend to the horizon at low water, clouds of stinging sand driven by the blast of the westerlies and even pockets of quicksand. The most dramatic feature of this coast is the remarkable tidal range, around 9 m (30 feet) in the **Southport** section, which results in vast expanses of foreshore being exposed at low tide. At **Formby** the character of the coast is provided by unstable dunes; we have already described how the drifting sand affected the town. Formby point is an unstable landmark, advancing and retreating as the sand shifts. There is severe erosion at Hightown, which is most extreme when high tides and westerly storms coincide.

Several resorts claimed an early stake in the tourist industry, but the explosion of the seaside bonanza came in 1871, with the introduction of the Bank Holiday Act, which enabled workers from the mills, pits and foundries to spend a weekend at the coast. Southport made its bid for fame, but **Blackpool** soon revealed a talent for doing things in the biggest, brashest and loudest manner imaginable. At first the holiday trade was quite refined, and in the eighteenth century guests at hotels such as Bailey's and Forshaw's were of 'the better kind'. Quite partisan in their loyalty to their chosen establishments, they would studiously ignore the guests from other hotels that they met when strolling on the grassy foreshore. In 1846, the railway arrived, making anything possible, and, in 1891, the mayors of twenty northern towns were present as the foundations of the Blackpool tower were laid.

Standing almost 158 m (519 feet) tall, the tower is a half-size replica of the Eiffel Tower. It was prefabricated in sections in Manchester and cost £45,000; it is still in a good condition despite the corrosive effect of the salt-laden winds. Illuminations were first staged at Blackpool to celebrate a royal visit in 1912, but it was not until 1925 that they became an annual feature – with the valuable role of extending the town's tourist season into the autumn months. All thoughts of energy conservation are forgotten as around 375,000 bulbs light up this ageing floosie of a resort. If the entertainment at Blackpool is wholesome, the bathing is not, for a survey by the Consumers' Association in 1991 revealed virus problems at the town's north, central and south beaches, where some samples of seawater contained as many as 20 viruses per 10 litres (18 pints).

At the northern end of Blackpool's tramway is **Fleetwood**, a ferry port with a fading fishing industry. Once there was a fleet of trawlers which fished in Artic waters, but now Fleetwood boats are reduced to working the dirty waters of the Irish Sea, which are flavoured by the differing discharges of the Mersey and Sellafield. To the north of Fleetwood is **Morecambe Bay**, which once supported a valuable shellfish industry. Pollution and changing tastes have undermined the cockle and mussel fisheries, and though shrimps are still popular, contamination has greatly reduced the catch. Despite such problems the bay supports a quarter of a million waders and a broad spectrum of species can be seen probing the mud-flats or roosting in the fringing salt-marshes.

At Morecambe, the development of the resort was organised around the less-than-daunting theme of being rather less brassy than Blackpool. The town receives around 300,000 residential visitors and more than a million day-trippers each year, but of late it has become rather scruffy and dowdy. On a coast strewn with sands, it has developed pebble beaches. But in 1991, the district council produced a plan to upgrade the resort as part of a programme for coastal defences; sands will be brought back and the central part of the promenade will be raised by 1.5 m (5 feet).

In Morecambe Bay, almost 200 km^2 (120 square miles) of sand are exposed at low tide. Travellers moving northwards from Lancaster into Cumbria would make the risky journey across these sands at low water, leaving from Hest Bank near Morecambe for Kents Bank near **Grange-over-Sands**. In Norman times, sand guides were provided by the local monastic houses, and later by the Duchy of Lancaster. The 'Queen's Guides to the

Sands' still exist, with a safe pathway being marked out by bunches of laurel thrust into the sands. Countless lives have been lost here, not all of them in the distant past. During the nineteenth century, the quicksands of the Black Scar hole caused some major disasters. Twelve people riding in a cart salvaged from a previous accident at the Black Scar were lost here as they rode to Lancaster Fair. A more agreeable effect of the bay is its moist and temperate climate, which allows native and exotic plants to flourish far beyond their normal northern limits. Grange began to develop as a resort in the last decades of the eighteenth century, and the shoreline has advanced considerably since the time of the early visitors. The railway arrived in 1857 and, despite the day-trippers arriving on the steamers from Morecambe, the resort developed in a genteel manner. More recently it has scarcely developed at all – and this is what its ageing population seems to prefer.

Barrow-in-Furness is quite different, a planned product of Victorian industrialisation. In the middle of the last century, there was nothing here but a village and a line of jetties visited by coasters collecting the locally mined iron ore. Blast furnaces came into operation in 1859, and by 1872 a town of 30,000 people had come into existence. By the end of the century this population had doubled, and the iron and steel and shipbuilding town, with scarcely a building as much as fifty years old, had filled much of its carefully prescribed plan. The world today, however, has little use for British ships, iron or steel. Millom, across the Duddon estuary, has a very similar past and problems.

A little further up the Cumbrian coast is the **Ravenglass estuary**, where the Rivers Esk, Irt and Mite meet the sea. This is a major breeding ground for black-headed gulls, for four types of tern, also oystercatchers, mergansers and shelduck. The number of gulls surviving here has declined dramatically and pollution is the prime suspect.

Next comes **Sellafield**, a PR-inspired renaming of old and unloved Windscale. Indeed, one doubts that there is a place so widely loathed on this or on any other coast. A global symbol of the foul-up and cover-up, Sellafield continues to convert the Irish Sea into a radio-active sewer. In the August of 1991, the government was advised by its advisory committee on nuclear waste that Sellafield should become the graveyard for the fleet of nuclear submarines. But there are no shafts large enough to accept the reactors. The cost of providing such facilities was said to be comparable to those associated with the Channel Tunnel.

St Bees Head is the most prominent natural feature on this section of the coast, with cliffs overlooking the sandy beaches which have formed above beds of boulder clay plastered down by the Lakeland glaciers. Whitehaven lies in the shelter of the headland, and though now often regarded as a depressed backwater, in the eighteenth century it almost exceeded Liverpool and competed with Bristol. The Cumberland coalfield runs from Wigton to St Bees Head. At the Dissolution, the Lowther family obtained the estates of St Bees abbey and, a century later, in 1636, a member of the family built a short quay for the export of coal. Three decades later, Sir John Lowther laid out **Whitehaven** to a rectangular plan and furnished it with a harbour. The coal port grew rapidly during the eighteenth century, when a trade based on exporting manufactured goods to the North American settlements and importing tobacco brought great wealth to the town.

Whitehaven never really recovered from the traumas of the American War of Independence. Deep water facilities were lacking, and the tobacco trade was lost to Glasgow, while the railways undermined the coastal coal trade – and then the mines themselves began to close. Further up the coast, **Workington** was the protégé of the Curwen family. They too had mines on their estates, and the town was expanded to serve the coal trade. In the Victorian period, Workington became a centre of the iron and steel industry, and so it emerged into the modern era equipped with those heavy industries which seem to be all past and no future.

Maryport was another family concern; here the Senhouses were the patrons. Once the River Ellen reached the sea at Ellenfoot but, in 1749, Humphrey Senhouse obtained an Act of Parliament which allowed the widening of the river mouth and the building of a pier. Shipbuilding developed, and the port became renowned for its clippers. Maryport reached the peak of its success as a coal exporting, iron importing and shipbuilding centre at the end of the Victorian era, but despite its decline, Maryport is not without its attractions.

The border between England and Scotland follows the main channel of the **Solway**, or so folk were brought up to believe, but even if this is the case, the regular shifting of this channel causes all manner of problems. Depending on the tide, the border can move by 1 km ($\frac{1}{2}$ mile) – and fishing laws in Scotland and England are different. At the time of writing, a timeshare company with fishing interests is asking the Scottish Court of Session to rule that the traditional 'haaf netting', practised in the Solway Firth since

Viking times, is illegal. The local salmon and sea-trout fishermen are defended by Annan council and a charter from James VI. For some years the English and Scottish fishermen have upheld the old definition of the border against bureaucrats and vested interests seeking to impose a fixed border following the mid point line through the Firth.

As the industrial ports on the Cumbrian coast grew, so they captured the shipping trade of towns along the Solway coast, like **Kircudbright** and **Annan**. **Dumfries** was used by Atlantic schooners, but the larger ships were unable to navigate the River Nith. The estuary of this river is a vital wintering ground for barnacle, greylag and pink-footed geese; they roost on the foreshore and graze in the natural salt-marsh which borders it. This is another coast of contrasts, for there are shingle beaches at Burrow Head, rugged headlands at Abbey Head, Borness Point and Mull of Galloway and sandy beaches backed by rolling dunes at Luce Sands and Torrs Warren to the west of Glenluce. At Portpatrick, where Scotland and Ireland are scarcely more than 30 km (20 miles) apart, the harbour was wrecked by storms and rendered useless in late-Victorian times, and only the tourist industry allowed the village to survive.

The coast running northwards from the Irish Sea ferry port of **Stranraer** to Clydeside is breezy and bracing. Stabilised by grass, the old dune systems along this coast provide some famous links golf courses, such as Troon. Probably the most widely known vista for followers of the sport is that of the island mass of Ailsa Craig as seen from the links at Turnberry. Long ago the sole tenant of this island survived by selling feathers from its great gannet colony. Ailsa Craig is a great boss of granite which was scoured by glaciers flowing from the Highlands across the dry bed of the Irish Sea, so that fragments of this distinctive rock are found in the glacial deposits far to the south in England. With the rise of Glasgow, towns like Ayr and Largs and several fishing villages discovered a new role as holiday centres.

Glasgow is not a natural harbour, and for centuries the city relied upon the outport of Irvine, far down the Clyde. Dredging during the eighteenth century made Glasgow accessible to shipping. The city became an importer of cotton and an exporter of iron and steel products, but the meteoric rise of Glasgow came with the expansion of the shipbuilding industry during the last third of the nineteenth century. With raw materials to hand and a workforce already versed in heavy engineering skills, Glasgow

The sea loch of Loch Long looking towards the head of the loch and the village of Arrochar

cashed in on the change from wooden-walled to iron-skinned ships. By Edwardian times, around a third of the world's tonnage of ships was Glasgow-built. The workers in this industry were cruelly exploited by their paymasters and now, following decades of contraction, the industry scarcely exists any more. Yet there is not the despondency and hopelessness abroad here as in Liverpool, though whether the proud city can complete its transition into a business capital equipped with modern industries remains to be seen.

Most great industrial towns stand amongst gentle agricultural countrysides, but Glasgow is blessed with a wilder setting. The industrial workers of the Clyde towns missed no opportunity to take their families away from the clamour and tenements, escaping on one of the many paddle steamers which sailed to places like

Dunoon or Millport. The most popular resort was Rothesay on the Isle of Bute, still served by a paddle steamer from **Wemyss Bay**. The railway station at Wemyss Bay was opened in 1903, and **Rothesay** reached the peak of its popularity in the 1930s; it never became raucous or blowzy, and endures as a traditional, but now jaded, family holiday centre. During its heyday, Rothesay would accommodate the families of one Clyde industrial centre after another as their holiday fortnights became due; first came Greenock, then Glasgow and then Paisley.

To the north of the Clyde estuary, the Scottish coast has a Highlands character and consists of high, rocky headlands separated by the deeply probing fingers of the ice-gouged sea lochs. Less dominating features of the coastal landscape than the towering mountains and narrow lochs are the raised beaches which line the shoreline, beaches which were uplifted and left high and dry as the great mass of Scotland recovered during the last 10,000 years or so, after having been pressed down by the weight of ice sheets and glaciers. It was on these beaches that the pitiful human debris of the Clearances settled after the evictions which followed the defeat of the Jacobite uprising at Culloden in 1746. The moorland was acid and barren, but kelp abounded in the sea and was rich in iodine, potash and soda. And behind the dunes which hemmed the beaches there were the narrow bands of the 'machair', a fertile, limy soil largely composed of the shells and skeletons of marine organisms which have been ground into a sand by the churning waves and blown inland from the beaches. Among those who cared, there were hopes that fishing and the gathering of kelp would form the basis of a more prosperous life for the people living on the shores of the Highlands and islands, but the kelp industry failed long ago, and fishing never really rewarded the expectations.

Long since denuded of good timber, the west coast lacked the raw materials of boat building. It bore the brunt of Atlantic gales, which forced the fleets to stay in harbour, while good natural harbours were in limited supply. **Ullapool** is the largest fishing port on this coast; its fishermen sell their catches of herring and mackerel to East European factory ships which anchor in the loch. The best harbour is near the southern margins of the region at **Oban**. With a direct rail link to Glasgow, this fishing and ferry port is a popular resort, and its population doubles during the holiday season. Dominating the town is the unfinished attempt to replicate the Colosseum, the brainchild of John Stuart McCaig, a

local banker, who launched the project to provide work for unemployed masons in the 1890s. At the end of the Road to the Isles is **Mallaig**, still a fishing port and served by ferries to several Hebridean islands. Mallaig, however, has fallen on hard times; with the decline in catches of herring, mackerel and prawns, the emphasis was switched to clams and scallops, but now the breeding grounds of these less familiar shellfish are being damaged by the nets of illegal cod trawlers. A Skye ferry also operates from the less picturesque port of **Kyle** of Lochalsh, plying across the narrow strait of Kyle Akin, which is scarcely half a mile wide.

Spectacular coastal scenery is commonplace along this coast and on **Skye** alone there are, amongst the cornucopia of scenic treats, the breathtaking views of the Cuillin Hills as seen looking over Loch Scavaig from Elgol, the columnar cliff formations at Kilt Rock, the shoreline castle of Dunvegan and the islands and inlets of Loch Bracadale. Indeed, all along the west coast of the Highlands it would be more difficult to find places where the scenery is merely mediocre than where it is good or spectacular.

Cape Wrath has been dreaded for the fury of its sea storms since sea-faring began; it forms a bold cornerstone of the Scottish mainland. The main centres of population on Scotland's short north coast are **Thurso** and **Douneray**. Thurso has a fine setting, with its sandy bay sweeping towards the promontories of Holborn Head and Dunnet Head, and it is renowned as a centre for sea angling. During the 1950s it doubled in size as houses were built for the nuclear power station workers at Dounreay. But both places have communities bitterly divided between those who stress the need for work and others who place more value on the need to live. Further along the coast is Scrabster with its ro-ro ferry to the Orkneys, which has been in operation since 1975. The coast has a turbulent finale in the treacherous waters of the **Pentland Firth**, bracketed on both the mainland and Orcadian sides by towering cliffs and sea stacks carved in old, rust-red sandstone.

Kilmaluag Bay at the northern tip of Skye, with the ruins of Duntulm Castle on the cliff

Chapter Eleven

JOHN O'GROAT'S TO LONDON

The east coast of Britain is often remembered for its low, crumbling shoreline, the clammy grey haar which rolls in from the cold North Sea and a holiday season which begins late and has weather more bracing than bronzing. In comparison to the west coast, pageants of majestic cliff scenery are fewer and further between, and there are by no means as many little salty seadog ports with vivid histories as on the south coast. Even so, the east coast does have some spectacular passages of coastal scenery, some invaluable refuges for wildlife and some settlements, including Whitby, Arbroath and Scarborough, which are wreathed in history. There are also places, such as parts of the East Anglian coast with their flat shores, vast skies and watercolour tints, that have an eastern ethos which is quite distinct.

Just to the south of the headland of **Duncansby**, the Stacks of Duncansby stand proudly off the east-facing shore. **Sinclair's Bay**, further down the coast, provides a contrast in scenery with a smooth strip of sandy foreshore curving for 6 km (4 miles) to end near Noss Head lighthouse. On high rocks just west of the lighthouse are the ruins of two castles standing almost side by side, Castle Girnigo and Castle Sinclair, both properties of the Earls of Caithness and both deserted around 1680.

Less than 30 km (20 miles) to the south of Duncansby is **Wick**, as grey as the sea beyond. It is an old town whose fortunes revived early in the nineteenth century, when the British Fisheries Society developed fishing installations on the northern side of Wick Bay at Pultneytown. Thomas Telford designed the harbour, and before the herring fishery gravitated to the larger ports of north-east Scotland at the end of the century, more than 700 fishing boats used the facilities here. Most of the boats were small, open-decked vessels, and when they packed the harbour the fisher lasses would work at a frantic pace on the quay, gutting the herring, salting them and cramming them into barrels for export. Now, the herring are almost fished-out, and a small fleet of seine-net boats searches for white fish, while the Caithness Glass factory provides a more promising source of employment. To the south of the town are the ruins of the fourteenth-century castle of Old Wick and the spectacular sea arch known as the Brig o' Tram.

The next fishing village of any size is **Helmsdale** at the outlet of **Strath Kildonan**. The Strath was the scene of a goldrush in 1868, one which produced more excitement than wealth. Next is **Brora**, a townlet with a diversity of activities. A coal mine was opened here in 1598, to provide fuel for evaporating salt; it was worked from time to time and reopened for a while in 1974. There is a distillery, a woollen mill, a rather moribund harbour and a more active tourist trade. We are now in the heartland of the estates of the Dukes of Sutherland, the scene of some of the most notorious events during the Clearances. Their former castle is at Dunrobin, just to the east of the resort of Golspie.

Dornoch is renowned for the sandy beaches at Dornoch Sands on the northern side of the Firth. It has a cathedral which was begun in 1224, was burned in 1570, and rebuilt and restored in the 1830s and 1920s. The little city is renowned in sporting circles as one of the cradles of golf. The game was being played along the coastal links before the start of the seventeenth century, and the Royal Dornoch course is a place of pilgrimage for golfing enthusiasts. Across the Firth is Portmahomack, which had a significant fleet of herring boats in the nineteenth century and which has another of Telford's harbours.

Invergordon on the **Cromarty Firth** has had fluctuating fortunes. The old castle town overlooked a superb natural anchorage and gained a harbour in 1828. Early in the present century it became a naval base and dockyard and saw great activity during the two world wars. The base closed in 1956, but soon gained a distillery as the town became the subject of a series of grandiose development plans, with oil rig and platform-building yards being established during the 1970s. Across the Firth and the narrow apex of the Black Isle are the neighbouring resorts of **Fortrose** and **Rosemarkie**, with the roofless ruins of a thirteenth- and fourteenth-century cathedral at the former, and cliffs cut in red sandstone at the latter. Between them is the headland of **Chanonry Point**, which juts across the narrow waters of the **Beauly Firth** towards another headland which carries the remarkably well-preserved Fort George artillery fortress. Built between 1748 and 1763, to the latest military concepts, this was the northern terminus of a chain of English forts created to divide the rebellious territory of the Highland clans.

Inverness, on the southern shores of the Firth, is the traditional focus of the Highlands, and controlled routeways at the northern end of the Great Glen. The settlement was probably centuries old when it was created a Royal Burgh in the twelfth century. Inverness was fortified and garrisoned by Cromwell in 1651, and the longstanding English presence in the town is said to be reflected in an accent and culture which contrasts with those of the surrounding lands. The Caledonian Canal reaches the Firth on the western fringes of Inverness. It provides a link between the eastern and western coasts of Scotland by connecting the Lochs Ness, Oich and Lochy, which occupy the great rip in the landscape formed by the Great Glen fault. The canal was begun by Telford in 1803, but not completed until 1847. Yet despite its setting and sea link, the character of Inverness is Highland rather than maritime.

The first sea port on the coast of the Moray Firth is **Nairn**, another twelfth-century Royal Burgh and medieval capital, and now a resort with fine sandy beaches. To the west of Nairn is Culbin Forest, planted on the mobile dunes of the Culbin Sands, which once drifted to engulf many a field, farmstead and hamlet. Salt-marsh fringes the shore of **Findhorn Bay**, where the climate of the Moray Firth is so mild that some forty-eight plant species are able to thrive here at the northernmost extent of their distribution. On the headland marking the western extent of **Burghead Bay** are the ruins of a great, fortified Pictish capital, while close by and in complete contrast are the rigidly planned outlines of Cummingstown village.

Rocky headlands shielding inlets and their fishing ports give the Moray Firth coast its character. During the herring boom, **Buckie** grew at a rapid pace while its neighbour, the old fishing port of **Findochty**, was colonised by a community of fishermen from Fraserburgh. Just along the coast is **Portknockie**, with the Bow Fiddle Rock offshore, a sea stack pierced by the waves to form a free-standing arch. Next is **Cullen** on a fascinating section of coast with sandy beaches, the Three Kings Stacks and the ruins of Findlater Castle on a rugged promontory. Cullen is in two parts, the old 'seatoun' on the shore and the cliff-top town set out to a neat plan by the Earl of Seafield in 1822 to house a community displaced from the village of Old Cullen. Like Cullen, the fishing village of **Portsoy** now functions as a holiday resort, and here again the town is on two levels, with the older houses down by the harbour. Ancient rocks of many types outcrop on the shore, including red and green serpentine, once quarried and exported to France and used in two fireplaces at Versailles.

Banff was not a product of the relatively recent herring boom, but an old regional capital and a member of the Hanseatic League of medieval trading towns; during the eighteenth century it became a fashionable wintering town for the Scottish gentry. **Macduff**, just across the Deveron estuary, is in the more familiar mould of a Moray port. An older fishing port, once known as

Doune, was expanded under aristocratic patronage in the late eighteenth century, and then prospered as the harbour at Banff silted up. Alexander Garden of Troup, the local laird, developed the twin villages of Crovie and Gardenstown during the 1720s, with Gardenstown being built on a narrow raised beach backed by towering cliffs. Here, in the vicinity of Troup Head, the cliffs are of the Old Red Sandstone, which was stained a deep brick red under the desert conditions under which the deposition took place. Some are conglomerates, with fist-sized cobbles embedded in a finer matrix. At the headland the cliffs are up to 120 m (400 feet) high, and are colonised by fulmars, skuas, kittiwakes and puffin.

At **Fraserburgh** and **Kinnaird Head** the orientation of the coast begins to change. The port was developed by Alexander Fraser of Philorth who, in 1546, obtained a charter allowing him to convert the little fishing village of Faithlie into a haven for ships rounding the headland. In the base of the family castle at Kinnaird Head was established one of Britain's first lighthouses, dating from 1787. Fraserburgh was one of the fishing ports of north-east Scotland which prospered as the industry became concentrated in a few large centres.

The main port on the Buchan coast to the north of Aberdeen is **Peterhead**. In 1593, the nobleman, George Keith, founded a village on the promontory here and, during the Napoleonic wars, Peterhead became established as the leading British whaling port. Later, this now unattractive role was lost to Norwegian whalers and those of Dundee, who were more receptive to the use of the harpoon gun as opposed to the hand-launched harpoon. But Peterhead, along with its east-coast neighbours, Fraserburgh and Aberdeen, expanded as a fishing port as the smaller fishing centres contracted, while during the 1970s it developed as a focus of the North Sea oil and gas industry. **Aberdeen** and the most interesting features of the Buchan coast – the former port of Old Rattray, the Ythan estuary, the blow hole at the Bullers of Buchan and the shifting sand dunes of Forvie – have already been described.

The coastal scenery between Aberdeen and **Stonehaven** is superb, with mighty cliffs carved in a variety of ancient rocks and stacks standing offshore in various places, like Muchalls, a spot where the seashore is accessible. At Stonehaven, the Highland Boundary Fault reaches the sea and the ancient schists, granites and gneisses yield to the younger, but still venerable, Old Red Sandstone. The town is a merging of separate planned settlements

created in the seventeenth and eighteenth centuries, but it was not until 1826 that Robert Stevenson provided the technology needed to remove a great mass of rock obstructing the harbour. Perched on tall red sandstone cliffs just to the south of the town are the ruins of Dunnottar Castle, the seat of Scotland's Earls Marischal and the place from which the Crown jewels and regalia are said to have been smuggled away from under the noses of Cromwell's forces in 1651.

Montrose is surrounded on three sides by water; to the east is the North Sea, to the south the outlet of the South Esk and to the west the tidal sand-flats of Montrose Bay, a gathering place for migrating wildfowl, such as the pink-footed goose. The town first came into prominence as a centre for smuggling, though during the eighteenth century it developed along more refined lines as a resort for the gentry of eastern Scotland. **Arbroath** became a resort much later. It was an important medieval monastic centre and sufficient survives to proclaim the grandeur of the twelfth- and thirteenth-century abbey. The abbot of Arbroath established an improved harbour here in the fifteenth century and, during the nineteenth century, Arbroath expanded as an important fishing port: home-cured smokies are still a speciality. Out to sea to the south-west of Arbroath is the infamous Bell Rock, named from the bell which the abbot of Arbroath had rung here as a warning to

The New Castle of Slains near Peterhead was home to the Earls of Erroll. Dr Johnson stayed here and thought it the ideal place to witness a sea storm, though Boswell could not sleep for the roar of the waves and his fear of ghosts

shipping. In 1807, Robert Stevenson began work on a lighthouse here; five generations of this family were engaged in constructing lighthouses around the Scottish shore, and the Bell Rock light-house is the oldest example still in operation. On the coast between Arbroath and Dundee is another famous east-coast links golf course, Carnoustie, whose patrons can gaze across the outlet of the Firth of Tay towards a course of even greater repute at St Andrews. Between Stonehaven and the English border some fifty links courses stand along the shore.

Road and rail bridges span the shores of the Tay at **Dundee**. The town rivalled Peterhead in the whaling trade and this trade survived for longer. It continued until the 1914–18 war, and when Dundee received its first street lights, they were designed to burn whale oil.

Bounded by the Tay and Forth, the small ports of the Fife peninsula have a long history of fishing and trading with the Low Countries. Today, the coastal scenery includes a strange blend of old fishing settlements which flourished with the rise of the herring fishery, including **Anstruther** and **Pittenweem**, and blackened coal and iron towns, such as **Kirkaldy**. The villages of the corner of the peninsula known as the 'East Neuk' prospered when the herring shoals deserted the waters of the west coast of Scotland and migrated to the North Sea. During the 1880s, the Anstruther fleet grew to number 221 boats, and 600 men were employed in the fishing industry, which began by harvesting the shoals in the Atlantic beyond the Outer Hebrides in the spring, and then followed them around the east coast until the Thames estuary was reached in the autumn. Now the town looks to tourism as its main source of income.

The Forth was spanned by a railway bridge in 1890, but road travellers used the ferry until the opening of the graceful road bridge between Queensferry and Inverkeithing in 1964. This route was used by medieval pilgrims bound for the shrine at Dunfermline, while other ferries sailed from Leith to Burntisland and Kinghorn. Like the northern capital of Inverness, Edinburgh seems to turn its face away from the sea. But on the shores of the Forth at Granton, Leith and Portobello the ethos is as salty as can be. **Musselburgh** and **Prestonpans** provided the capital with the food to stock its many oyster bars, though now the pollution of the Forth has killed the trade. But the old procession known as the 'Fishermen's Walk' still takes place at Musselburgh as the fishing families parade in traditional costumes. In the neighbouring vil-

The Forth road bridge, with the rail bridge to the right

lages of Cockenzie and Port Seton the end of the herring season was marked by the burning of an old boat, which was thought to dispel misfortune.

Offshore from North Berwick stands **Bass Rock**, a great plug of volcanic rock with sheer, black cliffs which are home to members of a gannet colony of around 20,000 pairs. On the cliffs just to the east of the town is Tantallon Castle, the fourteenth-century stronghold of the Douglas dynasty of Border barons. Moving southwards from Dunbar, travellers on the east coast railway are

249

given fleeting glimpses of the fine cliff scenery before the line diverts inland from St Abb's Head, where fishing boats would shelter in a small haven between the contorted rocks of the neighbouring cliffs. It returns to the coast at Burnmouth and runs towards Berwick-upon-Tweed and England along the shores of Lamberton Beach. Overlooking one of the few remaining great salmon rivers, the vulnerable border stronghold of Berwick is one of the best surviving examples of a fortified town, with the Elizabethan circuit of defences, constructed between 1558 and 1590, standing inside the medieval walls.

The quiet coast between Berwick and Amble provides no foretaste of the chaos of squalor to come on the industrial section of the Northumberland coast. Separated from the mainland by tidal sand-flats, Holy Island or **Lindisfarne** became an advance post of Celtic Christianity during the seventh century as St Aidan, a follower of St Columba, began the conversion of pagan Saxon Northumbria. A few miles down the coast and further out to sea lie the twenty-eight islets of the **Farne Islands**, which have existed as a seabird sanctuary of major importance since their purchase by the National Trust in 1925. On the adjacent shore is **Bamburgh**, where a craggy volcanic ridge supported the little fortified settlement which served as the capital of Dark Age Northumbria. Much later, a Norman keep commandeered the Castle Rock, though the medieval castle we see today owes much to a remodelling by Lord Armstrong in 1890. Another great castle, Dunstanburgh, stands on cliffs overlooking **Embleton Bay**, a few miles further south. It was built in 1313 for the second Earl of Lancaster, and was slighted by the Yorkists during the Wars of the Roses. The coast proceeds in an alternation of cliffs and dune-fringed bays to **Alnmouth** and **Amble**, where fishermen still use open cobles as they hunt the salmon bound for the Rivers Aln and Coquet.

From here to the estuary of the Tees the character of the coastal landscape has been transformed by industrialisation. The sands of the shore are blackened by the dust and slurry of coal mining and the air itself is acid- and smog-laden. Near the medieval castle town of Newcastle coal outcropped in the valleys, allowing it to be easily quarried rather than mined, and colliers bound for London were operating well before the close of the Middle Ages. Little wharves began to line the banks of the Tyne, and as the surface deposits were exhausted, so water-powered pumps were developed to drain the new shaft mines. During the reign of Elizabeth I, the coal shipments from Newcastle had risen from 33,000 tons to

163,000 tons per year, and in 1684, some 616,000 tons of coal were shipped from the Tyne. Life for the crews of the colliers which coasted along the North Sea seaboard may have been less glamorous than that experienced by the sailors manning privateers, but it was still fraught with danger. Daniel Defoe recorded the events in 1692, when a fleet of 200 colliers returning to Newcastle from Yarmouth was struck by a storm off Winterton, and fragmented as vessels raced for the shelter of Yarmouth and King's Lynn. At the same time a southbound fleet of colliers, grain ships and merchantmen was caught in the onshore gales off Winterton Ness, and driven on the beaches. The death toll from the storm was about 200 ships and 1,000 sailors.

Newcastle had passed into the control of its Company of Hostmen or coal lords, and at the start of the seventeenth century it expanded beyond its cordon of old walls. But this growth was modest in comparison to that which took place in Victorian times. In 1825 the first public railway was opened between Stockton and Darlington, in 1829 George and Robert Stephenson produced a much improved locomotive, the 'Rocket', Newcastle gained a rail link to Carlisle in 1838 and the High Level Bridge spanned the Tyne in 1849. Meanwhile ship-building and iron-smelting added their contributions to the changing coastal landscapes.

These changes obliterated the character and most traces of what had gone before. During the Middle Ages, **Blyth** existed as a small community of fisherfolk and salt-makers who worked in the quiet seaside setting between dunes and salt-marshes. During the eighteenth century, the village grew as a port for the export of locally mined coal, and then in the 1880s, a great complex of piers and breakwaters were developed, so that by the end of the century, Blyth was exporting four million tons of coal each year.

Tynemouth had an abbey in pre-Viking times, and in the eleventh century a priory church of St Albans was established in a setting where the the wind was said to toss masses of sea spray over the buildings. Late in the eighteenth century, the village at Tynemouth discovered a new role as a resort, a role which was buttressed in 1867 with the arrival of the railway. Winter gardens, a ballroom and an aquarium were built above the cliffs as Tynemouth set out to become the 'Brighton of the North'. It failed, and so too did **Whitley Bay**, though this late-Victorian resort came a little closer and still attracts large numbers of holiday-makers from Glasgow. **North Shields** began as a fishing hamlet which provided fish to Tynemouth Priory, and then rivalled Newcastle as an export outlet for the locally produced wool and hides. In the course of the nineteenth century, North Shields was transformed by the growth of its harbour installations, though during the first half of the century it was a popular abode for shipping barons, sea captains and the professional classes.

Spectacular and traumatic growth also affected the estuary of the Tees. The growth of **Middlesbrough** was quite phenomenal. At the start of the nineteenth century, there were just four houses here, but within just a century, a town of 91,000 inhabitants had arisen. In 1829, a group of Quaker industrialists extended the Stockton to Darlington railway into coastal salt-marshes here, and constructed large wharves for the export of coal. Two years later, a town with a symmetrical plan was set out behind these wharves, thus creating one of the few great industrial towns to develop without growing around a much older nucleus. The railway made Middlesbrough possible, but as the efficiency of the system increased, so the coastal trade declined. Under the entrepreneurship of Henry Blockow, an immigrant from Mecklenburg, Middlesbrough responded by adopting a new role. Ironstone was available in the Cleveland Hills, and in the second half of the century the town emerged as a major iron-smelting centre, with its iron works filling the ground between the town and the river.

Today, the coast between Amble and the Tees is of more interest to the industrial archaeologist than the nature lover. It provides an alternation of sand dunes, slag heaps, reed beds, chemical plants, derelict shipyards and run-down resorts. It has a character, albeit a mournful one, but it also has contamination of the land, sea and air at the most scandalous and unpardonable levels.

Redcar has no artificial harbour, but a haven which is shielded by outcrops of rocks running seawards; the little port now serves as a resort for Cleveland. Between **Marske** and **Saltburn** there are fine, level sands, which were once considered, but later rejected, by Malcolm Campbell when he was looking for a site upon which to attempt the world land speed record. Saltburn was developed in Victorian times by the entrepreneur, Henry Pease, as a holiday centre for the fast-growing industrial towns of Teeside. But when they stopped expanding then so too did Saltburn. It arose beside the old fishing and smuggling centre of Old Saltburn, where The Ship inn dates from the sixteenth century, and stands close to a Victorian mortuary, a stark reminder of the countless vessels which were wrecked on this unforgiving coast. There is a brief return to the world of industry at the old steel-making village of Skinningrove, a place which almost died and then revived after the closure of local iron mines. The cliffs at Boulby, just along the coast, have been hewn and gouged, for here the varied strata contain iron, limestone, alum, jet and coal, while underground and beneath the seabed there is a potash mine producing raw materials for the Teeside chemicals industry.

Staithes is one of the oldest and most attractive fishing villages on the east coast. As is so often the case, it is in two parts, with the old village sitting on a cramped cliff-foot bench, and the more recent additions on the higher ground. The harbour is not ideal, and the old settlement itself was vulnerable to storms from the north-east. Just along the coast is **Port Mulgrave** which, though isolated now, used to ship ironstone to Teeside in Victorian times. At **Runswick Bay** the old fishing component again forms the lowest level of the village, the successor to the original settlement, which collapsed into the waves in 1664. Now fishing itself is but a memory in this little tourist and retirement centre. The nearby cliffs offer rich geological interest and include jet shales, beds containing ammonite fossils and others of compacted clay. At **Kettleness** the Romans built one of their east-coast signal stations when the declining empire was threatened by Saxon raiders. Presumably the intention was to alert civilians and troops stationed inland, and to relay a warning to the great garrison and city of York. The cliff-perched village of alum miners here was largely destroyed during a storm in 1829.

No east-coast town or village has more historical interest and character than **Whitby**. The town is associated with the explorer, Captain James Cook, but local affection also embraces Caedmon, a humble herdsman who discovered a great gift for poetry, and who became a monk at St Hilda's Abbey during the seventh century. This double monastery (for monks and nuns) was established in 657, by Hilda, a disciple of the Roman missionary, Paulinus. It was at a synod here in 664 that the destiny of English Christianity was decided when King Oswy of Northumbria chose in favour of the Roman rather than the Celtic Church. The abbey was destroyed by Viking raiders in 867, but re-established two centuries later by the Norman knight, Reinfrid. The old town nestles below the abbey, and the fish pier marks the site of the eighteenth-century fish market. The harbour has been protected by piers since the sixteenth century; during the eighteenth century, Whitby became a noted whaling port, and as this industry de-

The ruins of St Hilda's abbey at Whitby

clined, so the herring fishery was exploited. There is still a fleet of about seventy fishing boats, most of them small cobles. Much of the town is composed of an attractive jumble of tightly packed dwellings and steep, winding alleys, but there are also elegant Victorian terraces. These are a legacy of the entrepreneur, George Hudson, who developed Whitby as a resort when the railway arrived in 1847.

The coast south of Whitby offers splendid cliff scenery, marred in places by that recurring blight of the Yorkshire coast, the caravan park. **Robin Hood's Bay** is a cliff-perched former fishing and smuggling village which was nibbled away by the sea until the building of a new sea wall in 1975. Local legend claims that, in 1893, the bowsprit of a storm-tossed brig burst through the window of the Bay Hotel. Another Roman signal station was built at Ravenscar, while nearby the Peak Fault marks the boundary between the Lias rocks, which have provided so much detailed and varied coastal scenery, and those of a less diverse composition, which produce the smoother coastlines to the south. Wooded

The rising tide invading Filey Brig

cliffs are found at Hayburn Wyke, where a beck makes a pictures-que descent to the beach via a gorge and waterfall.

Like Whitby, **Scarborough** offers much more than the average resort. The cliff top overlooking the town is dominated by the Norman keep of the great royal castle, built here in the 1130s, while within the grounds of this castle an Iron Age settlement and a Roman signal station have been excavated. A Viking village at Scarborough is said to have been destroyed by the forces of the Norwegian King, Harald Hardrada, during the invasion of 1066. It may have been during the building of the castle that a planned town was set out on the lower ground of the peninsula bearing the castle, and archaeologists have recently explored the twelfth-century town ditch which was dug across the neck of the penin-sula to defend the civil settlement. At the peak of Scarborough's medieval prosperity the town's waterfront extended around the edge of South Bay for almost 640 m (700 yards), the first quay being built in the thirteenth century. The town flourished as a market centre which exported local farm produce, as a fishing port

A traditional seaside scene at Filey, where the fishing boats on the sea front recall the old economy

and as an industrial settlement famous for the production of decorative, green-glazed pottery. Although the medieval layout is reflected in the street plan of the older part of the town, history is less insistently obvious than at Whitby, and the main character of Scarborough is provided by the ambitious tourist developments of Victorian times, such as the Grand Hotel of 1867 and the Spa Pavilion of 1876.

Yet another Roman signal station stood on cliffs above the base of **Filey Brigg**. The Brigg is a peculiar and spectacular formation, formed from a bed of hard, lime-rich grit which has resisted the sea more stoutly than the cliffs which once stood above it, while just to the Filey side of the Brigg are unstable, dangerous and rapidly eroding cliffs of boulder clay. Filey is a former fishing village which attempted to develop in a rather restrained and refined manner.

Between Filey and **Flamborough Head** lies one of the finest sections of the British coastline, rich both in cliff scenery and in birdlife. The chalk of the Yorkshire Wolds forms cliffs which are sheer and towering, and gannets, puffin, kittiwake, razorbill, guillemot, fulmars and herring gulls can all be seen with ease from

the cliff top path running through the RSPB reserve. Towards Flamborough Head the cliff scenery becomes more detailed, with caves, sea stacks and arches all in evidence. The headland was guarded by the great ancient earthwork known as Danes Dyke, while the village of Flamborough developed much later, as a combination of the fishing quarter and the agricultural settlement which grew around St Oswald's church. In the churchyard lie the bodies of scores of local fishermen and sailors from distant places who have perished on the dangerous shores around the headland.

At **Bridlington** the scenery takes a different turn, for this old herring fishing port is now an out-and-out holiday resort catering for most of the less sophisticated needs of the Leeds–Bradford area. Here we must say our goodbye to bold cliff scenery, for the remainder of the east coast is formed in a tamer mould. The fast-crumbling clay cliffs of **Holderness**, the shifting spit of **Spurn Head** and the fluctuating fortunes of the past and present Humber ports have already been described, and so we move on to the Lincolnshire coast – but not without mentioning the remarkably beautiful if economically distressed Humber road bridge. Opened

in 1981, to supersede the ferries which had plied the Humber since time immemorial, the 1,400 m-long (4,600 foot-long) bridge has failed to generate the expected traffic. Perhaps this could be related to the fact that nobody got round to providing the roads needed to serve it?

Grimsby became one of the most successful of the North Sea fishing ports, its good fortune being said to be due to the accidental discovery of sole-fishing grounds by a Brixham trawler which had been blown off course. With the arrival of the railway in 1848, Grimsby was able to despatch fresh fish to London. Later in the century, the port captured much of Hull's cod trade, when the line fishers of Grimsby were able to keep their catch alive in the holds of their boats and transfer the fish to floating chests on the waterfront.

The graceful Humber road bridge

Towering chalk cliffs at Bempton, where the Yorkshire Wolds meet the sea

The Lincolnshire coast is of the most modest scenic interest, being composed of low cliffs of soft boulder clay, sand dunes and mud-flats which offer little resistance to the sea. Many parts of the coast, such as the stretch near **Sutton**, were badly damaged in the great storm of 1953, and the erosion continues. Massive sea defences have been built at **Hornsea** and **Withernsea** and new works were recently completed near the jaded resort of **Mablethorpe** for tourists from the Midlands. **Skegness** is yet another fishing village which grew as a resort in Victorian times. Its promoters showed considerable initiative, for in the early years of the present century they were able to capitalise on a climate which visitors of a less enthusiastic kind might describe as chill and windy, and promote it as being 'so bracing'.

During the last ice age, the southern half of the North Sea existed as cold, windswept marshland, and during the thaws the eastward-flowing rivers flowed across the plains and swamps as tributaries of the Rhine. But when the ice masses melted and the sea level rose, the land beyond and within **The Wash** was inundated. The soft coast of East Anglia has been shaped by quite recent erosion; between **Weybourne** and the Norfolk Broads about 5 kilometres (about 3 miles) depth of coastline has been eaten away, though in other places there has been growth. Fossil cliffs lie some distance inland between Hunstanton and Weybourne, where sand spits and salt-marsh have grown to advance the shoreline. The present cliffs at **Hunstanton** are not rugged, but peculiarly colourful, displaying layers of white chalk, red chalk and biscuit-brown Carstone. Around the edge of the Fens, successive seabanks mark the stages in the reclamation of farmland from sand-flats and salt-marshes.

King's Lynn grew amongst swampy lagoons on higher ground provided by disused salterns of the salt-making industry, and was developed as a market centre by the bishops of Norwich from the start of the twelfth century onwards. The part-time salt-workers were also shepherds, and so Lynn became a port for the export of local wool. Its prosperity grew rapidly, so that early in the reign of King John only two or three English ports were paying higher customs duties. (The same king saw the baggage train containing his treasure disappear into estuarine quicksands nearby in 1215, when travelling from Lynn to Lincoln.) The town was walled from the outset, with old sea banks being redeveloped as walls and then furnished with four timber towers; they were rebuilt and provided with corner bastions at the time of the Civil War. King's

Lynn suffered greatly from the decline in the wool and broadcloth export trade at the end of the Middle Ages, and never discovered a new role of equal importance. Much of the surviving character dates from the eighteenth century, which resulted in Lynn being chosen as the location for a movie about the American War of Independence.

The stretch of soft cliffs at Hunstanton soon gives way to coastal salt-marshes. At **Brancaster Bay** the coastal strip assumes a zoned appearance, with a fossil cliff-line standing well inshore, then a zone of long-cultivated former sea-bed supporting old agricultural and maritime villages, then a band of reclaimed salt-marsh, which serves as pasture, and finally, a strip of natural or semi-natural

The neatly planned resort and multi-coloured cliffs at New Hunstanton

261

salt-marsh between the land and the sea. In early medieval times, the village of **Salthouse** was the collection centre for salt produced from brine at various places along this coast. Several villages, such as **Cley** and Nelson's birthplace of **Burnham Thorpe**, were ports until the advance of the shoreline left them high and dry. **Overy Staithe** was developed as an outport as Burnham became stranded, while the port of **Blakeney** was choked by the growth of the spit of **Blakeney Point**. After the port-turned-resort of **Cromer** there are cliffs composed of soft glacial drift. In places they are as high as 60 m (200 feet), but they offer little resistance to the sea, and scores of homes and hamlets have made the swift and fatal journey from cliff to beach. At **Happisburgh** the coastline is formed by dunes rather than cliffs, and it was at **Sea Palling** that the high spring tides driven by gales from the north breached the coastal defences in 1953. With high water at the coast, the East Anglian rivers were unable to drain into the sea and they burst their banks. Some 307 people lost their lives and 32,000 were rendered homeless.

Overlooking the estuary of **Breydon Water** are the most evocative of all Roman forts of the Saxon shore ruins. The bastioned walls of Burgh Castle stand on elevated ground which commands fine views across the reclaimed marshes with their drainage windmills near the convergence of the Rivers Yare and Waveney.

As we have seen, **Great Yarmouth** was founded on sand and shingle deposited in a section where the coast is growing rather than retreating. **Lowestoft** became a significant fishing port in the fourteenth century, and was one of the leading centres of the herring fishery of the eighteenth century. With the arrival of the railway in 1847, it captured the commerce of its smaller rivals. Lowestoft suffered badly from bombing during the Second World War, and later from the general contraction of the fishing industry, although it still supports a fleet of deep sea trawlers which quest for cod, haddock and turbot.

In Suffolk the coast bears frequent testimony to the wilfulness of the waves. **Dunwich**, as we have seen, passed from greatness to oblivion long ago and **Walberswick**, its successor, now has more artists than professional mariners. **Blythburgh** is another place where high ambitions were dashed by fickle currents, and at **Covehithe** the soulful beauty of the great church ruins speak of a parish devoured by the sea. **Southwold** sought to overcome the misfortunes from silting by cutting itself a new harbour and by competing with the Dutch fishing fleet in the

A windmill amongst reclaimed salt-marsh at Cley in Norfolk

The imposing church at Covehithe, reflecting the former prosperity of a parish partly lost to the sea

harvest of the herring shoals. But by 1800, the new harbour was choked by silt and Southwold found a new future as a seaside resort and watering place. At all these places the entrepreneurs believed they could predict and control the ways of Nature. Their mentality was adopted by those who built a Magnox nuclear reactor at Sizewell, near Dunwich, in the 1960s, and who then decided to add a Three Mile Island-style reactor here in 1987, just nine months after the Chernobyl disaster.

Much of the character of the East Anglian shore is provided by the currents which sweep sand and shingle along the coast in a clockwise direction, gnawing into the soft cliffs of boulder clay and building south-curving spits across the mouths of the rivers. Such a spit diverted the course of the Alde, and so gradually disposed of the commercial ambitions of **Orford**. Here we can gain a reliable impression of the rate at which such features can grow, for ten miles of sand and shingle have been added to the little snout which existed when the royal castle was built here in 1162. At **Felixstowe** and the modern container port of **Harwich** the tale of decline is reversed, for they have grown by shunning the outmoded practices of the older and prouder ports.

The Essex coast south of **Clacton** has deep inlets formed by drowned river valleys, muddy creeks, expanses of sand, reclaimed salt-marsh and islands. Brent geese roost on **Foulness Island** and the profusion of waders and seabirds resulted in the threat of birdstrikes being one of the important reasons for the rejection of the proposal for the building of a third London airport on the Maplin sands.

Finally, we come to **Southend-on-Sea**. Visitors on the seafront have no reason to suspect that the roots of the settlement were provided by the Cluniac monastic house of Prittlewell priory, which was founded here at the start of the twelfth century. During the eighteenth century, Southend grew quite rapidly at the southern end of the old monastic grounds as a settlement of oyster fishermen who supplied the greedy London market. Adventurous visitors arrived by ship from the capital, and were carried across the sands on the backs of fishermen. Some of them liked the fresh and breezy coast on London's doorstep and decided to settle here, and elegant Regency terraces and squares were built. The tone was stylish but staid. But then the railway arrived in 1856, and with the establishment of Bank Holidays in the 1870s the destiny of the town was seen to lie in a different direction. Southend was ideally placed to entertain the swarming day-trippers and holiday-makers. It gained the world's longest pier and a reputation for clamour, drunkenness and brawls between the rival East End tendencies. Brighton now had somewhere to look down upon.

SANDS AND TROUBLED WATERS

Nature created a coastline of the most remarkable diversity, with cliffs and beaches carved in rocks of every age, hue, texture and toughness, and with other shores edged with sand-flats, salt-marshes, dunes, spits, shingle and lagoons. The waters offshore were populated with numberless shimmering shoals of herring, sand eels, pilchard and scores of other species. The cliffs became home to raucous, tumultuous flocks of seabirds, zoned in colonies and speckling the cliff faces in a white confetti of wheeling, plunging, soaring life. Above the dunes, meanwhile, the sky was stippled by the flickering wings of terns, while the estuaries and coastal marshes echoed to the honking, quacking and piping of geese, ducks and waders in a plethora of different types, each one exploiting its own little niche in the setting. The coast offered men, women and children sufficient beauty and interest almost to overwhelm their senses, with an endless array of places where they could marvel at the wonders of the natural world and find the troubles of day-to-day life dwarfed by the overpowering ethos of land, sea and sky. Yet now the landscapes, which seemed so vast and so invincibly charged with wholesome natural energies, have been defiled and contaminated. Human arrogance, greed and stupidity have, in the course of little more than a century, made ugly scenes which were millions of years in the making, and have rendered sick and depleted forms of wildlife which have existed since long before the dawn of mankind.

Often the damage is insidious, and the only evidence of the poisoning is found in the corpses of seabirds or abandoned nests of sterile eggs. But in some places man has changed the whole character and configuration of the shore. The uncontrolled population growth in the south-east of England, and the insatiable demand for resources which results, has led not only to the destruction of most of the good countryside in the home counties, but also to assaults on landscapes far away. Now coastal super-quarries, which will devour the unspoilt coasts of northern Britain, are muted as the answer to southern needs for roadstone and building materials. At present, such a quarry operates at Loch Linnhe and, at the time of writing, there are proposals from Redlands Aggregates to quarry Lingerabay in the National Scenic Area on the south-east tip of Harris, and from Sullom Voe Aggregates to quarry at Haggrister in Shetland, while experts have predicted the opening of as many as seven coastal super-quarries in the north.

When the time to decide arrives, it is so often the case that officials, who have previously mouthed all the correct platitudes about environmental concern, decide that they are unable to stand in the way of 'progress'. They do not pause to explain what is progressive in a society which makes no attempt to adjust its population to the capacity and quality of the environment which it inhabits, and which blunders remorselessly onwards towards increasing unemployment and the inability to support its overblown population in settings rendered devoid of any natural character or humanity.

It would be hard now to find a qualified biologist who will not agree that mankind is destined for extinction within the next few thousand years – or less. Those who are disillusioned and ashamed by our tenancy of the planet might find comfort in the notion that within a few brief moments of geological time there will be a return to the natural order. Man will be no more. Wave and tide will crumble and reshape the shores, so that all that will remain of the coastal refineries, caravan parks and housing estates will be flattened morsels of piping, hub caps, roof tiles and the like buried in the uppermost rock strata of the Quaternary age. Meanwhile, from the surviving relics of their populations, fish, seabirds and any sea mammals which have survived will multiply to reclaim the shores and coastal waters from which their ancestors were evicted. So once again there will be glorious natural settings all vibrant with harmonious life.

But there is a flaw in this scenario, for man has left a curse which will endure long after his departure. Moving clockwise around our shores from the capital, there are nuclear establishments at Dungeness, Winfrith, Hinkley Point, Oldbury, Berkeley, Trawsfynydd, Wylfa, Capenhurst, Springfields, Heysham, Sellafield, Chapelcross, Hunterston, Dounreay, Torness, Druridge Bay, Hartlepool, Sizewell and Bradwell. In addition there are naval bases, including Devonport, Faslane and Rosyth, associated with nuclear vessels. The decommissioned nuclear submarine, *Dreadnought*, has been stored afloat since 1983 because nobody knows what to do with the lethal thing. According to Greenpeace, 'seven Western nuclear submarines have been lost in circumstances surrounded by secrecy since 1963. Some thirty-seven reactor-based incidents are thought to have occurred aboard Soviet nuclear vessels alone since 1954. Between eighty and a hundred nuclear vessels are at sea at any one time.' The threat to marine life comes not only from the nuclear reactors which power these boats, but also from the nuclear missiles which they carry.

The history of coastal nuclear power stations has followed a familiar course. It begins with assurances from the powerful nuclear interests and their scientists that the operations are perfectly safe. Accidents follow and the sequence of foul-up, hush-up and cover-up is initiated – and it is left to agencies independent both of the industry and government to reveal the awful extent of the contamination. Sellafield, as dirty as a fishwife's apron, was said to be 'clean'. In the days before its cosmetic renaming it was Windscale, where a fire in 1957 released radiation causing from thirteen to more than a thousand fatal cancers, depending which estimate is believed. Even so, there was much official surprise and doubt expressed when it was shown that traces of radioactive caesium-137 were evident in windblown silt from Cumbrian beaches and in the waters around the Western Isles. Now it is known that this contamination is swept all around the coast of Scotland, then down the east coast of England as far as the Thames estuary, across the southern North Sea basin and along the shores of Denmark and Norway. A strange way to gain our revenge on the Vikings.

In September of 1990 the government announced that £1.7 billion would be spent on building Hinkley C, an American-style pressurised water reactor, on the Somerset coast. More than 20,000 people had written letters of protest to the preceding public inquiry. Doubtless they realised that their letters would be as effective as a cat-flap in an elephant house, but they wrote them all the same. And presumably these people – and countless more – would have preferred to invest in a form of energy that was clean and renewable. In fact such an alternative exists, in the form of wave power, for which an efficient method of exploitation was developed by Professor Salter at Edinburgh University in the 1970s. The reason why this research was killed off was explained by Professor Jeffrey in *Environment Guardian*: 'the Department of Energy is full of nuclear protagonists, and those seconded to help the development of renewable energy sources did not always leave their nuclear commitment behind.' The Energy Technology Support Unit, charged by the government with finding alternatives to nuclear energy, has its headquarters at the secretive atomic energy headquarters at Harwell – and has given no indication of being a turkey about to vote for an early Christmas.

Barring the more spectacular type of tragedy, nuclear materials poison in ways that can only be traced by scientists and measured by statisticians. With over-fishing, the evidence is more forthright:

the fish stocks disappear. The existence of over-fishing has been plain for a long time, for the partial suspension of fishing during the two world wars was followed by short-lived returns to heavy catches, since the shoals had been given time to regenerate in a more natural manner. Virtually every palatable type of fish and shellfish is over-fished and it is easy to imagine a situation in which the over-fishing proceeds until fishing itself becomes uneconomic, and then comes to an end as all the boats go out of business. In reality the situation is more complicated. Fish which devour smaller fish, plankton and other marine organisms are part of a food chain, and if they are effectively exterminated then the whole balance of marine life is destabilised, and there may be an uncontrolled explosion of other forms of marine life.

Over-fishing is not the only ill to affect fish stocks; poisoning by pollution is another threat. Shellfish are exposed to the tin-based TBT anti-fouling compound applied to boats and a noxious cocktail of industrial effluents is highly detrimental to fish caught commercially. Fish caught in the waters between Anglesey and Morecambe Bay have been found to be contaminated with high levels of mercury and organic chemicals known as PCBs. The decline in the fertility of the North Sea seal population has also been attributed to PCBs. In August 1991, a meeting of marine scientists was told that the effects of pollution on fish stocks in the North Sea appeared to be worse than had been thought. Heavy metal pollution seemed to be most severe at certain hotspots in industrialised estuaries, but the most worrying feature was the disease caused by organic pollutants, such as pesticides and herbicides, which reached the sea from the land.

Succeeding generations have regarded the sea as a place where filth could be dumped and forgotten. At first this did not matter too much, for the quantities were relatively small, and the poisons relatively unsophisticated. Until well within living memory, farming was a wholesome activity which renewed fertility by recycling organic nutrients, and which allowed livestock to grow in a natural manner. Residues from farming seep into the streams and groundwater, then enter rivers and are thus conveyed to the sea. Into the sea come pesticides and antibiotics as well as steroid compounds and salts of copper and zinc, fed to animals to enhance their growth rates. These all come in tiny quantities, but are then concentrated in the bodies of plankton, which are consumed by small fish which in turn are eaten by larger fish and seabirds. Arriving in far larger quantities from the run-off and seepages are the nitrogen and phosphate fertilisers, which over-enrich the estuarine waters and cause potentially toxic blooms of algae. British farming is said to be responsible for about twelve per cent of the nitrate load entering our waters. Sometimes the poisoning is returned to man, the part-perpetrator, by the consumption of shellfish which has consumed the toxic mobile plant forms generated by the over-enrichment.

More emotive when displayed on our television screens are the effects of oil pollution. Thus far the worst scenario – a blow-out on a North Sea oil well – has been escaped. Meanwhile, the British public has become accustomed to, but not hardened to, the sights of dead or dying seabirds washed ashore with oil-fouled plumage. A tiny proportion of affected birds are cleaned and restored to the wild. But most die, either because their plumage can no longer insulate them against the cold or because their attempts at preening cause them to be poisoned. In an imperfect world, any urbanised maritime country can expect to suffer from spillages at refineries and pipeline terminals, while the growth in the size of the supertankers gives these vessels an almost uncontrollable momentum. But big business is not the only culprit. Much of the fouling of our shores is caused by masters who furtively flush tanks and discharge waste oil from their vessels into the sea, and by backyard mechanics who pour used engine oil down water drains.

Marine sites for the dumping of sewage sludge exist off Dundee, Edinburgh, Humberside, Exeter and Plymouth; colliery waste is dumped in the sea off Tyneside and sites for the dumping both of sewage and industrial waste are found off Glasgow, Tyneside, Teeside, London and Southampton. In 1991, the Marine Conservation Society demanded that warnings to bathers should be erected beside each of the 250 coastal pipelines which were currently discharging raw sewage into the sea.

All the other countries of the North Sea basin regard the practice of direct dumping at sea as unnecessary and barbaric. The problem of chemical discharges from pipelines is of an even greater magnitude; everything from arsenic to plutonium and from mercury to cadmium is discharged in this way. Long ago, industrialists could be forgiven for imagining that the contaminants would be dispersed in the sea and rendered harmless. But for years it has been known that the highly toxic and persistent materials accumulate in food chains and become progressively concentrated in living bodies: every reader of this book has DDT in his or her body fat, and this inheritance will be passed on to future generations. Each factory operator involved in the discharge of heavy metals and other contaminants has a fairly good idea of the consequences, yet the discharges continue, and are allowed to continue.

Were the sewage that is dumped uncontaminated by chemical waste it could usefully be recycled for use as an organic fertiliser on the land. In 1990 the British government was compelled to yield to EEC pressure to ban the dumping of sewage sludge at sea. Thus the water companies responsible were obliged to discover new ways of disposing of the annual production of 11.7 million tons of effluent. The majority have opted for land-based incineration – but this introduces the problem of the fall-out of contaminated ash from the smoke stacks, for the sludge contains viruses, industrial chemicals, heavy metals and drug residues.

Of all the problems concerning the pollution of the British coastline, the fouling of holiday beaches has been the most heavily publicised. In 1985, a European Bathing Water Directive, which sought to establish tolerable standards of health at bathing beaches, came into force. This Directive had been signed by Britain as long ago as 1975; fifteen years of relative inactivity and evasion followed. As a result, in 1990, the British government was warned that it faced prosecution over a stunning total of 138 beaches which failed to meet the safety standard. The problem confronting bathers had been evaded by the government subterfuge of not designating some of the most popular but most polluted resorts as bathing beaches. Meanwhile, action was delayed so that potential shareholders in water companies destined for privatisation would not be alarmed by the costs of cleaning the beaches. Amongst the beaches identified as unclean by the European Commission were those at Brighton, Broadstairs, Great Yarmouth and Southend.

Resorts which failed the test did not suspend their efforts to attract visitors, but frenziedly jubilant PR activity was associated with the modest number of beaches which obtained the coveted European Blue Flag awards for cleanliness. A great many of the 446 eligible British resorts did not even apply for consideration, their authorities being fully aware of the filthy state of their beaches. No resorts in the north-west of England applied. In 1990 a total of just twenty-nine resorts succeeded in reaching the required standard. In 1991, this figure rose to thirty-four.

Here, it might have appeared, was good cause to trumpet about the rising standards of cleanliness on British beaches. Not so. In the August of 1991, the Consumers' Association revealed that the Department of Environment had declared that many beaches reached European standards – while knowing full well that they did not. It had not been revealed that many beaches had failed the virus component of the tests. Included amongst the failures were the so-called blue flag beaches at Bridlington North, Eastbourne and Filey.

Faced with the information that citizens were exposed to the risk of infection which involved not only unpleasant illnesses, but also very serious ones, such as meningitis and hepatitis, the authorities concerned sought refuge in subterfuge. A spokesperson at the Department of Environment did not express alarm at the danger to the public, or announce an end to duplicity and the launching of a forceful programme of public-spirited action. Instead, she observed that to obtain virus-free beaches one would have to shoot all the seagulls. She did not care to mention that seagulls scarcely seem to be in short supply at Bexhill-on-Sea, where not a single virus was found in the 10-litre (18-pint) sea water sample.

For many years, politicians of a certain persuasion have sought to frighten the electorate with images of a Europe composed of faceless bureaucrats, all tensed and ready to pounce on our cherished institutions and sovereignty. Often such xenophobic claims feil on fertile ground, for at times in the past the Channel has been our salvation. It has allowed the British to avoid conquest by powerful neighbours; to stand apart from European affairs and develop global contacts, and then to intervene at will to restore the continental balance of power. But for how much longer can the British public be persuaded to loathe and fear a European institution when it has become as plain as a pikestaff that the members of that institution care far more deeply and more sincerely about our health, hygiene and social welfare than do our elected national leaders?

The British coast has become a source of national shame, but it has also served as a testing-ground where claims and policies are vindicated or refuted. In case after case officialdom has been found guilty of failure and duplicity, while in case after case truth and action have only resulted from the intervention of investigative journalists, environmental organisations, such as Friends of the Earth and Greenpeace, and other whistle-blowers. But now that the secrets have been revealed, who can we blame but ourselves if the ruination of the coastline is allowed to continue?

SOME USEFUL BOOKS

Balchin, W.G.V., *The Cornish Landscape*, Hodder & Stoughton, 1983.

Barrett, John and Yonge, C.M., *Collins Pocket Guide to the Sea Shore*, 1958.

Bellamy, David, *The Wild Coast of Britain*, Webb & Bower, 1989.

Beresford, M.W. and St Joseph, J.K.S., *Medieval England, An Aerial Survey*, 2nd edn, Cambridge University Press, 1979.

Brentnall, Margaret, *The Cinque Ports and Romney Marsh*, John Gifford, 1980.

Calder, Nigel, *The English Channel*, Chatto & Windus, 1986.

Dymond, David, *The Norfolk Landscape*, Hodder & Stoughton, 1984.

Fisher, J., and Lockley, R.M., *Sea Birds*, Collins New Naturalist Series, 1954.

Greenpeace, *Coastline, Britain's Threatened Heritage*, Kingfisher Books, 1987.

Newton, Robert, *The Making of the English Landscape: The Northumbrian Landscape*, Hodder & Stoughton, 1972.

Peck, Edward, *North East Scotland*, Bartholomew, 1981.

Ravensdale, Jack, and Muir, Richard, *East Anglian Landscapes*, Michael Joseph, 1984.

Saunders, David, *Seabirds*, Hamlyn, 1971.

Seymour, John, *The Companion Guide to the South Coast of England*, Collins, 1975.

Smith, Ian, *Yorkshire Coastline*, Sandhill Press, 1990.

Somerville, Christopher, *Britain Beside the Sea*, Grafton, 1989.

Steers, J.A., *The Coast of England and Wales in Pictures*, Cambridge University Press, 1960.

Williams, Herbert, *The Pembrokeshire Coast National Park*, Webb & Bower, 1987.

Yonge, C.M., *The Sea Shore*, Collins New Naturalist Series, 1990 edn.

INDEX

Aberdeen 164–5, 168, 170, 175, 246
Aberystwyth 228
Abinger 138
Ailsa Craig 237
Alde, River 35
Aldeburgh 35
Alfred, King 134, 167
Alnmouth 169, 250
Amble 250
Anglo-Saxons 129–32, 133, 134
animals 95–9, 104, 226, 231
Annan 237
Anstruther 248
Appledore (Devon) 217–18
Arbroath 243, 247–8
arches 18–19
Arrochar 238
Arundel 138, 139

Bamburgh 250
Banff 175, 245
Bangor 231
Barnstaple 217
Barrow-in-Furness 235
Barry 223
Bass Rock 249
Beachy Head 202
Beaulieu 42
Beauly Firth 115, 244
Beaumaris 139, 231
Bempton Cliffs 51, 52–3, 56, 259
Berkeley 219
Berrow 220
Berwick-on-Tweed 144
Bideford 217
Birchington 194
birds 45–64, 78–80, 94–5, 101, 102, 103,
    105–15, 118–19, 193, 219, 226, 231, 234,
    235, 237, 247, 249, 250, 256–7, 265
Blackpool 190, 233–4
Blakeney 42, 263
blow holes 18
Blyth 251
Blythburgh 150, 263
Blyth, River 149
Bodiam Castle 139
Bognor 203
Boscastle 217
Bosherton 17, 18, 226
Bournemouth 185, 187, 205
Bradwell 130
Bramber 138, 139, 203
Brancaster 130, 261–3
Braunton Burrows 32, 218
Breage 213
Brean Down 40, 220
Breydon Water 263
Bridgwater Bay 41, 109, 219
Bridlington 10–11, 17, 257, 274
Brighton 138, 182–5, 202, 203
Brig o'Tram 243
Bristol 205, 215, 221–2, 232
Bristol Channel 31, 218
Brixham 4, 208

Broadstairs 185
Brora 243–4
Brownsea Island 143
Buckie 175, 245
Bude 170, 190, 217
Burgh Castle 130, 131, 263
Burghead Bay 245
Burnham Thorpe 263
Butley, River 35
butterflies 67–71

Cabot, John 168, 205, 222
Caerleon 128, 132
Caernarfon 129, 132, 139, 230–1
Calshot 143
Camber Castle 143, 200
Canterbury 41, 138
Cape Cornwall 215
Cape Wrath 241
Cardiff 132, 223
Cardigan 32, 227–8
Carisbrooke Castle 130
Carnoustie 248
caves 18, 19
Cawsand 179, 209
Cemaes Head 228
Chanonry Point 244
Chatham 144, 146
Chesil Beach 9, 36, 119, 207
Chester 128
Chichester 115, 126, 203
Christchurch 138
Chronicle of Matthew Paris 166
Cinque Ports 136, 152, 166, 179, 195, 198,
    199, 200, 202
Clacton 265
Clevedon 221
Cley 263
Cliffe 41, 197
Clifton 222
Clovelly 170, 190–1
Clyde estuary 125, 237–9
Cockenzie 249
Colchester 122
Colwyn Bay 186, 188
Combe Martin (Hangman's Hills) 18
Conwy 140, 231, 232
Conyer 41
Corfe 205
Cormorant Rock 228
Cornwall 3, 11–12, 13, 21, 22, 30, 31, 53,
    65, 67, 70, 98, 121, 123, 124, 166, 169–
    71, 180, 190–1, 209–13, 215–17
Cove 170
Covehithe 16, 149, 263, 264
Criccieth 229
Cromarty Firth 109, 244
Cromer 263
Crovie 246
Cuckmere, River 21
Culbin Sands 32
Culborne 218, 219
Cullen 174, 245
Cummingstown 245

Dart, River 21, 142
Dartmouth 168, 171–2, 208
Deal 126, 142, 143, 179–80, 182, 195
Defoe, Daniel 37, 151, 152, 154, 162–3,
    163–4, 177, 182–3, 251
Devon 4, 8, 11, 18, 19, 21, 32, 42, 124,
    166, 179, 190–1, 208–9, 216–18
Devonport 209
Diamond, John 178, 179
Dinas Head 227
docks 193, 196–7, 203–4, 209, 237–8
Dornoch Firth 109, 110, 244
Dorset 5–6, 7, 16, 24, 36, 119, 122, 167–8,
    185, 205–8
Doune 245–6
Dounreay 241
Dover 31, 128, 130, 135, 137–8, 143, 149,
    152, 161, 194, 196–7, 198
Dumbarton, Castle Rock 125
Dumfries 23
Dunbar 126
Duncansby 24, 243
Dun Carloway broch 132
Dundee 246, 248, 272
Dun Fother (Dunottar) 125–6, 247
Dungeness 36–7, 146, 152, 198, 199
Dunottar Castle 125–6, 247
Dunster 219
Dunwich 149, 150–1, 161, 263, 264
Dymchurch 198

Eastbourne 138, 202, 274
East Somerton 169
Edinburgh 248, 272
Edward I, King 37, 139, 140, 153, 154,
    162, 188, 228–9, 230, 231
Elegug Stacks 225
Embleton Bay 250
estuaries 42–3, 77, 104–15
Exeter 272
Exmoor 218, 219
Exmouth 208

Fairbourne 228
Fair Isles 50
Fairlight Glen 16, 200, 201
Falmouth 143, 190, 209
Farne Islands 98, 118, 250
Farnham 139
Felixstowe 31, 265
Ferriby 122
Fiennes, Celia 37, 222
Filey 17, 256, 274
Findhorn Bay 245
Findochty 245
Firth of Forth 110, 248–9
Firth of Tay 110, 111
fish 82, 92–3, 95, 97, 98–9, 104–5
Fishguard 227
fishing 165–6, 168–75, 193, 198, 205, 208,
    209, 210–11, 213, 227, 231–2, 236–7,
    239, 241, 243, 245–6, 248–9, 253–4, 259,
    264, 270–1
Flamborough Head 11, 17, 18, 51, 256–7
Fleetwood 234

Folkestone 16, 197–8
Foreland Point 218
Formby 32, 233
Fortress 244
Forvie 32, 157, 246
Foulness Island 265
Fowey 166–7, 209
Fraserburgh 175, 246
Frome, River 24, 203

Gardenstown 174, 246
Geoffrey of Monmouth 123
Germoe 213
glaciation 7, 20, 21, 225, 239, 260
Glamorgan 124, 157–9
Glasgow 236, 237–8, 272
Goudhurst 179
Gower Peninsula 224
Grange-over-Sands 234–5
Grassholm 51, 56
Gravesend 143
Great Yarmouth 143, 151, 165–6, 168, 263
Green Bridge of Wales 18, 225
Greenland 50, 55, 108, 110, 111, 113, 118
Grimsby 155, 169, 259
Guildford 139
Gurnard's Head 124, 215

Hadrian's Wall 129
Hallsands 208–9
Hampshire 6, 33, 42, 63, 130
Happisburgh 263
Harlech 139, 228–9
Hartland Point 217
Harwich 265
Hasted, E. 41
Hastings 16, 31, 135, 136, 138, 152, 179, 198, 199, 200–1, 202
Haverfordwest 227
Hawkhurst 179
Hayburn Wyke 255
Hebrides 59, 98, 113, see also Isle of Lewis; Isle of Skye
Hedon 163–4
Helmsdale 174, 243
Hengistbury Head 122–3, 204–5
Henry VIII, King 142, 143, 144, 147, 204, 206, 211
Hinckley Point 220
Holderness 10, 157, 257
Holyhead 132, 230
Hornsea 260
Horsey 32
Hull 161–3, 164, 222
Humber estuary 110, 111, 122, 152, 154–6, 258–9, 272
Hunstanton 186, 260, 261
Hurst 33, 143
Hythe 135, 146, 152, 198

Ilfracombe 218
Invergordon 244
Inverness 244–5
Ireland 11, 21, 31, 56, 94–5
islands, formation of 23–4
Isle of Anglesey 11, 13, 54, 124, 128–9, 231
Isle of Lewis 53, 132, 175
Isle of Man 13, 54
Isle of Portland 36, 133, 206–7
Isle of Purbeck 19, 205
Isle of Sheppey 193

Isle of Skye 20, 67, 161, 241
Isle of Thanet 194
Isle of Wight 19, 23–4, 50, 68, 130, 135, 138, 143, 203

John o'Groat's 24

Kenfig 157–9
Kent 16, 28, 31, 36–7, 41, 50, 104, 126–8, 130, 134, 135, 152, 193–9
Kettleness 156–7, 253
Kilve 7, 219, 221
King's Lynn 260–1
Kinnaird Head 246
Kipling, Rudyard 178
Kirkaldy 248
Kirkcudbright 237

Lamb, Charles 179
Lancashire 12–13, 22, 32, 190
Lancaster 132
Land's End 23, 24, 30, 50, 213, 215
Langton Matravers 205
Leland, John 123, 159, 167, 216, 224
Lewes 138, 139, 182
Lincolnshire 11, 123, 259–60
Lindisfarne 115, 180, 250
Linney Head 224–5
Liverpool 215, 222, 232–3
Lizard Point 213
Llandanwg Chapel 157, 228
Llandudno 186–8, 189
Llanvigangel-y-Traethau 229
Lleyn Peninsula 122, 229–30
Loch Long 238
London 143, 144, 161, 193, 272
longshore drift 29–30, 34, 36
Looe 190, 209, 210
Lowestoft 31, 151, 169, 263
Lulworth Cove 5, 6, 18–19, 24, 25, 68–9, 205–6
Lundy Island 51, 56, 218
Lybster 174
Lydd 198, 199
Lydstep Head 10, 224
Lyme Regis 16, 207–8
Lymington 204
Lympne 128, 130, 198
Lynmouth 218
Lynton 218

Mablethorpe 11, 123, 260
Macduff 245–6
Mallaig 175, 241
Manorbier 225
Margate 194
Marske 252
Maryport 236
Mawddach estuary 228
Mawes 211
Meaux Abbey 155, 156, 161
Medway estuary 109, 144, 146
Menai Straits 11, 23, 129, 230, 231
Mersey estuary 232–3
Mevagissey 169, 210–11
Middlesbrough 252
Milford Haven 6, 21, 146, 226
Minehead 218–19
Montrose 109, 247
Moray Firth 32, 245
Morecambe 22, 32, 113, 234, 235
Morfa Dyffryn 228

Mousehole 170
mud 38–40, 75–7, 94, 104, 234
Musselburgh 248

Nairn 245
New Brighton 233
Newcastle 250–1
Newfoundland 55, 118, 168, 172, 205
Newgale 225
Newhaven 202
Newlyn 170
Newport (Wales) 219, 223
Newquay 19, 170, 171, 190, 216
Norfolk 3, 31, 32, 39, 42, 130, 149, 165–6, 169, 260–3
Norman Conquest 135–6
North Berwick 249
Northern Isles 54, 98 see also Orkneys; Shetlands
North Shields 251–2
nuclear power 235, 264, 269–70
Oban 23, 175, 239
Oldbury 219
Orford 34, 35, 138, 151, 264–5
Orkneys 19, 32, 50, 94, 118, 153, 157, 241
Orwithfleet 155
Ouse, River (East Anglia) 63, 109, 115
Ouse, River (Sussex) 139, 202
Overy Staithe 263
Oxwich 224

Padstow 170, 173, 190, 216–17
Patrington 163
Peacehaven 202
Pembroke 226–7
Pembrokeshire 1, 6, 10, 15, 16, 18, 45, 58, 67, 124, 180, 224–7
Pendennis 143, 211
Pentland Firth 241
Penwith peninsula 215
Penzance 190, 213
Perranporth 216
Peterhead 9, 175, 246, 247
Pevensey 130–1, 135, 136, 138, 152
Pevensey Levels 200, 202
piracy 166–8, 210
Pittenweem 248
plants 64–67, 68–9, 69–70, 71, 83, 84, 101, 102–3, 104, 116–18, 220, 221, 231
Plymouth 122, 144, 146, 204, 209, 272
pollution 95, 97, 193, 220, 231–3, 234, 235, 248, 271–4
Polperro 169, 171
Poole 122, 138, 167–8, 171–2, 205
Porlock 218, 220
Portchester 130, 131, 138, 203
Port Errol 174
Porth Clais 227
Porth Dinllaen 230
Porthmadog 229
Porth-y-Nant 230
Port Isaac 169, 217
Portishead 222
Portknockie 245
Portmahomack 244
Portmeirion 229
Port Mulgrave 253
Portquin 216, 217
Portree 161
Port Seton 249
Portsmouth 138, 146, 203–4
Portsoy 245

277

Prestonpans 248
Prince Regent 183–4, 203
Pultneytown 243
Pwllheli 229
Pytheas 213

Radipole 185
railways 185, 197–8, 211
raised beaches 21–3
Rame Head 124
Ramsgate 194
Rattray 35–6, 246
Ravenglass 129
Ravenglass estuary 235
Ravenscar 254
Ravenser/Ravenserodd 154–5, 161, 163
Reculver 28, 126, 127, 130, 194
Redcar 252
Rhee Wall 198, 199
Rhuddlan 188
Rhyl 186, 188–9
Richborough 126, 127, 128, 130, 194, 196
Robin Hood's Bay 254
rock pools 82–93
rock types 10, 11, 15–17
Romans 126–33, 137, 181
Romney 135, 152
Romney Marsh 36–7, 104, 146, 152, 177, 178, 179, 198, 200
Rosemarkie 244
Rother, River 36, 139, 153, 199
Rothesay 238–9
Ro Wen bar 228
Royal Military Canal 146, 198
Rumps, The 121, 124
Runswick Bay 156, 253
Russell, Richard 182
Rye 37–8, 138, 139, 146, 152, 198, 199–200, 201

St Abb's Head 250
St Austell 210
St Bees Head 129, 235–6
St Brides Bay 225
St David's 15, 180, 181, 227
St Govan's Head 225, 226
St Ives 23, 171, 215
St Kilda 46, 50, 51, 55, 58
St Leonards 201
St Mawes 143
St Michael's Mount 180, 213
Salcombe 209
Saltburn 185–6, 252
Salthouse 263
salt-marshes 34, 38–42, 101–4, 202, 228, 234, 260, 262–3
sand 28–9, 31–3, 74, 115–19, 228, 231, 234–5, 244, 245
Sandgate 143
Sandown 143, 195
Sandsfoot 143
Sandwich 134, 135, 152, 161, 194–5, 198
Scarborough 181, 185, 243, 255–6
Scilly Isles 53, 57, 62, 67, 70, 213

Scotland 3, 9, 11, 20, 21–2, 23, 24, 32, 35, 51, 59, 64, 94, 95–6, 111, 112, 113, 114, 125–6, 157, 169, 171–5 see also Hebrides; Northern Isles
Scrabster 241
sea bathing 180–3, 185, 186
Seaford 202
sea levels 7, 21–4, 225
Sea Palling 263
Segontium fort 129, 230
Sellafield (Windscale) 235, 268, 270
Selsey Bill 122, 203
Severn, River 104, 105, 222–3
shellfish 76–8, 80, 81–2, 84–92, 110, 193, 234, 241, 248
Shetlands 50, 55, 56, 57, 58, 59–60, 95, 118, 268
shingle 28, 29, 33, 35, 74, 198, 199
Shoreham 202–3
Sidmouth 208
Sinclair's Bay 243
Sizewell 264
Skara Brae 153, 157
Skegness 11, 123, 260
Skokholm Island 226
Skomer Island 45, 226
smuggling 41, 176–80, 199, 200, 209, 247, 252
Solent, The 24, 146–7, 203
Solva harbour 225
Solway Firth 113, 115, 236–7
Somerset 7, 40, 109, 218–21
Southampton 138, 139, 204, 211, 222, 272
Southend 194, 265
Southport 12–13, 233
Southsea 143
South Shields 128
Southwold 149–50, 263–4
spas 180–1
Spithead 24, 142, 203
spits 33, 34–6, 42, 151, 264–5
Spurn Head 257
stacks 19, 24
Staithes 253
Start Point 208
Stonar 194
Stonehaven 5, 125–6, 244, 246–7
Strangford Lough 94–5
Stranraer 237
Strath Kildonan 243
Suffolk 16, 31, 35, 149–51, 165–6, 263–5
Sule Skerry 58
Sunk Island 155
Sunthorp 155
Sussex 15, 16, 21, 30, 36–7, 115, 122, 130–1, 135–6, 152–4, 179, 182–5, 199–203
Sutton (Lincolnshire) 260
Swaine, Joseph 179
Swanage 205
Swanscombe 193
Swansea 223

Tees, River 105
Teesmouth 51

Teignmouth 208
Tenby 19, 224
Thames estuary 68, 127, 128, 143, 146, 193–4
Tharlesthorp 156
Thurso 174, 241
tides 4, 30–1, 103, 104, 222–3
Tilbury 143, 144, 193
Tintagel 123, 217
Tobermory 175
Tor Bay and Torquay 4, 208
tourism 180–91
Tre'r Ceiri 229
Troon 237
Tynemouth 251
Tywyn 228

Ullapool 175, 239

Vikings 125, 126, 133–4, 135, 136

Walberswick 149, 263
Wales 1, 4, 6, 10, 11, 15, 16, 17, 18, 19, 32, 45, 58, 67, 111, 122, 124, 139, 157–9, 180, 186–90, 224–7
Walmer 143, 195–6
Walney Island 61
Walton Castle 130
Walton-on-the-Naze 185
Wantsum Channel 126, 152
Wareham 167
Wash, The 63, 104, 109, 111, 260
Watchet 218, 219
wave action 8–15
Waveney, River 21
Wemyss Bay 239
Wensum, River 21
Weston-super-Mare 185, 221
Westward Ho! 2
Weybourne 260
Weymouth 143, 185, 206
Whitby 243, 253–4
Whitehaven 236
Whitley Bay 251
Wick 19, 243
William the Conqueror 135–6, 137, 202
Winchelsea 36, 37–8, 139, 152–4, 158, 161, 164, 198, 199
Winterton 169, 251
Wiseman's Bridge 225
Withernsea 260
Wolltack Point 124, 125
Workington 236
worms 75–6, 82, 89
Worthing 203
Wyke 161–2

Yorkshire 10–11, 17, 52–3, 68, 115, 132, 135, 156–7, 253–9
Ythan estuary 32, 110, 115, 157, 246

Zennor Head 215

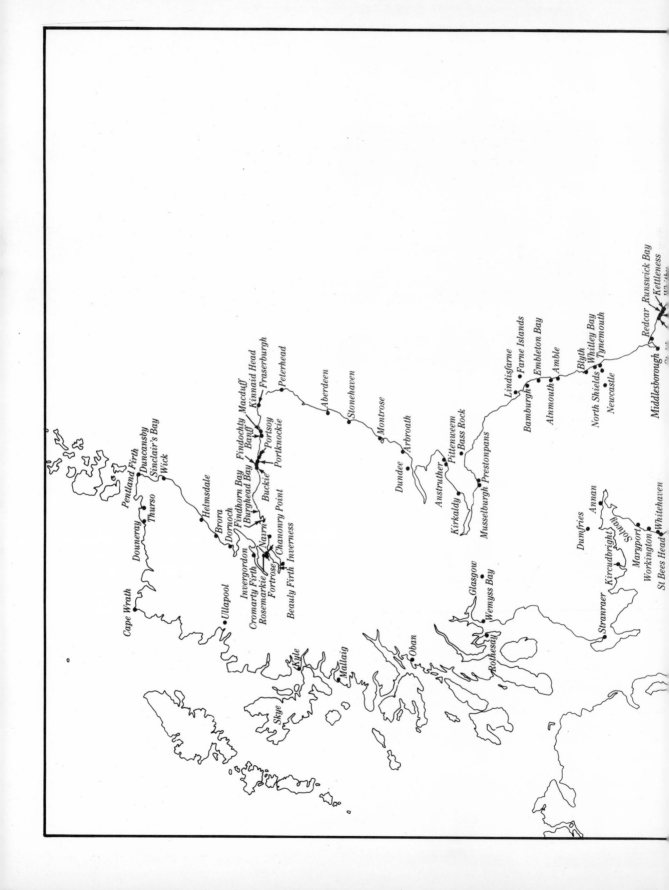